BLACKGANG CHRONICLES

THE LIFE AND TIMES OF FREDDIE

BOOK NO 2

JAMES SUNDFORS

TABLE OF CONTENTS

DEDICATION

This book is dedicated to my wife, Sandra, who has been my life partner for more than 50 years! She is the reason I was able to attain many of the goals that I set for myself at an early age. She always encouraged me to pursue my goals regardless of days we had to spend apart. She was also quick to rearrange her schedule so that she could accompany me to countries around the globe and become more educated in her own right.

I also dedicate this book to my maternal grandmother, Nana, who gave me the tools to apply to any job using hard work and a commitment to excellence. These lessons, learned at a young age, became a beacon to guide me through my career. Thank you, Nana, for everything that you shared with me.

I am deeply appreciative of my editor, Rodrigo Munoz, who has a gift for bringing out the common sense in my writing and making it more readable. Thank you, Rodrigo, for all your time and effort on my behalf.

Finally, I need to thank Don Gibbs, the leader of my writing group. He is a PhD and developed the Chinese Studies program at UC Davis. Don is a very educated man, but also has a gift for writing in a classic conversational manner. He instilled in our group the desire to write with clarity about ourselves. I thank him for his honest and helpful manner with this book.

PROLOGUE

This second book about Fredrik "Freddie" Johansson paints the life and times of a young man starting out his career as a marine engineer and as a member of the Blackgang. Freddie has graduated from the California Maritime Academy (CMA) just in time to man the ships for the Vietnam War sealift. His dream of getting his Chief Engineer's license is well underway after a couple years of sailing aboard Victory ships. The Vietnam War is now in full swing and the need for war goods is constant, resulting in high demand for seasoned marine engineers like Freddie.

The goal of this writer is to expose the general public to the life of those colorful hard-working seamen of the Blackgang. You are witnessing this all through the eyes of Freddie, a marine engineer, as he pursues his quest to advance his license and sail on as many ships as possible. The lifestyle depicted is that of a mid-1960s graduate of the California Maritime Academy, whose career transcends the period of time where steamships were the norm and motor vessels were few. He ships off the West Coast of the United States out of the port of San Francisco. Most of his ships are heading towards the Orient and are in some manner associated with the Vietnam sealift.

The advent of containerization begins about this time, and pretty soon Freddie is able to gain exposure to that phenomenon and watch as the marine industry changes dramatically due to the ideas presented by Malcom McLean, the godfather of containerization. You will learn about the steamship companies' struggles to survive and adapt, and about some companies which failed after making the wrong decisions. You will also see these changes in the industry as they apply to the Blackgang personnel and their jobs aboard the ship.

In concert with these shifts in the seagoing part of the industry, you will also witness many changes in the people going to sea. As the generation which manned ships during WWII phases out of the workforce, the rough-and-tumble Licensed and Unlicensed Blackgang are replaced by men and women who are able to develop lives and families ashore. The lifestyle of the 1950s and '60s fades away in the face of massive changes in both the industry itself and the men and women who run the ships as Blackgang members.

I have inserted hand sketches of different systems and equipment to provide a visual representation of some of the equipment and machinery I write about. I have also provided a Glossary in the back of the book to clarify some of the nautical terms used in my writing.

This book is a work of fiction inspired by my experiences going to sea and working ashore. If any of its characters in any regard resemble anyone living or dead, this is purely coincidental.

James Sundfors
Retired Chief Engineer

As discussed in the first book of *The Life and Times of Freddie*, the makeup of the Blackgang members aboard any one ship was diverse in all manner. Their socio-economic backgrounds varied widely, as many of the Unlicensed Blackgang were marginally educated. The engineers, for the most part, were from maritime academies, so they had both a high school and a college education. However, there were also engineers who did not have the financial means to go to a maritime academy but needed work, had picked a seagoing life, and had the desire to be an engineer. These "hawsepipe engineers" were veterans of years spent living at sea. Many left home to sail so that they could support their families.

The other part of the equation was race, with Filipinos, Native American Indians, East Indians, Greeks, Italians, Irish, and Swedes represented on different crews. In the 1960s there were also a few Blacks who sailed in Blackgangs as engineers, while most Blacks were Unlicensed Wipers.

The biggest divide was education and different individuals' opinions in regard to the government and the world at large. The Unlicensed, some of whom were semi-illiterate, gained all their information from their shipmates and from the union which they belonged to. They were strong union men who understood the need for unions, which made clear the hours of the day sailors worked and the food they ate aboard ship. The other benefit a union offered was the promise of someone to back them up when problems arose aboard ship which might affect their pay or capability to remain aboard.

The Blackgang was run as a hierarchy in which whoever had the most seniority could approach the First Engineer or Chief Engineer with a problem (beef). Many had limited education and probably did not graduate from high school. Going to sea was a plum job as it provided a place to sleep, food to eat, and care of a doctor as needed. The work schedule was fixed, and all they had to do was adhere to the rules of the Engineering Department and the union they belonged to.

By now Freddie had been out of CMA for more than two years, and had witnessed the diversity of such crews firsthand. He'd also tried to educate himself about the seagoing lifestyle and learn which leaders best handled the mix of personalities aboard ship. In the case of the Blackgang, the leader was usually the First Engineer, who in turn reported to the Chief Engineer. Freddie only had the three years at CMA and two years at sea to fall back on, so to expand his skills further he looked towards those who ran a happy ship, kept a clean engine room, and were fair to all the members of the Blackgang.

The most striking thing he noted was that the most successful heads of Engineering Departments were those First and Chief Engineers who could bring out the best in each of the crew. An individual might smell, or be belligerent, or be unable to talk intelligently, but each was capable of doing some job better than any of the rest of the Blackgang. For example, someone might be a good welder, even if he was not an engineer. Another might be a good painter, able to prepare, prime, and paint any surface. Some were excellent carpenters, and could even make furniture. The best Watch Standing personnel were those who had a knack for running machinery, understanding when a motor was running too hot, or hand-firing a boiler with grace of hand and foresight.

The best of the First Engineers and Chief Engineers that Freddie had been shipmates with kept a happy ship and a clean engine room in which all the machinery ran well and there were few breakdowns. From these folks, Freddie had picked up some tips about being a leader. Most never yelled or got disturbed when something went wrong. They were even-tempered and greeted each and every member of the Blackgang with a warm "Good morning," or "How ya doing?" Such a leader made you feel as if he was your favorite uncle or grandfather who was always looking to make your day. This fortified the feeling in Freddie of having a home away from home on the ship that he was assigned to.

Since he lacked the time or experience to allow him to get a permanent position aboard a ship, Freddie's jobs all came out of the union hall, where his shipping card gave him a chance to compete with other union members who were looking for work. Freddie knew the routine, and how to gauge his chances of getting a job he wanted to apply for. He had paid his initiation fee, annual dues, and other costs to the Marine Engineers Beneficial Association (MEBA), so he was a "member in good standing." The only thing which sometimes prevented him from getting a job was if someone was holding a very old shipping card on account of having spent more time waiting on the beach than Freddie.

Some of the Blackgang had colorful pasts and personal experience with the law, but chose the life at sea to escape the environment, family, or conditions that led them to be less than friendly. These men emitted a sense of danger and no one approached them unless they sent out a friendly message. They did their work, ate alone, and spent their off hours reading or sitting out on a bench looking at the sea. If engaged in conversation some of them could recite poetry or bits of history they knew. If they liked you, for instance if they were your watch partner, they might even share the facts of their background and why they chose to go to sea to make a living. Again, such a loner might be picked by the First to work alone, weld, or do some piping if he had the talent.

The lesson was that if you were to sail as a First or a Chief then you had to overlook the covering of the individual—their outward characteristics—and instead concentrate and direct whatever talents the person provided to the betterment of the ship.

A few topics, such as politics, marriage, and such, were taboo with some of the Blackgang. Neutral subjects included ports they had visited, past voyages they had sailed on other ships, or where the best girls were in each port. Some of the Blackgang had no other home, and they were often most content aboard ship, trusting few who they knew in the US home port. They might even have a wife in a foreign port and spend their vacations there. Some were married in more than one port and spent all their time on a ship to pay for their upkeep. Many Blackgang members had past loves and marriages which had turned out badly, and so were not too fond of the gentler sex.

Conditioning yourself to live the life of a Blackgang member could even limit your social graces when you were off a ship and living in the world of your US home port. This difficulty could be avoided by staying within a community of other seamen who all entertained themselves in a particular bar, restaurant, or union hall.

In summary, the breed of the Blackgang ranged from the ultra-educated to the almost illiterate.

Would you agree that exposure to all kinds of ships is a good thing? After almost two years, Freddie realized that he had no time on his license working an AC-powered ship. He had received his Second Assistant Engineer's license, so his next job had to be aboard a ship which belonged to that category.

His shipping card hadn't spent very much time ashore, so he wouldn't be able to be too picky. He had burned through some money in the time he took off to study and take his license exam, so he knew he should be putting some funds away and trying to get a ship as soon as possible. It was not uncommon for seamen to have only pocket change left when they finally got a new job. Once aboard a ship, the seaman had a room, food, and work, plus the capability to earn a good bit of money within a short period of time.

As a rule, most tried to avoid ships on the shipping board which got passed up by the old-timers, especially those which paid about the same as a Watchstanding Third Assistant on a Victory ship. Wages were based upon horsepower-tonnage, so the larger the ship and the higher its horsepower, the more money a sailor would make.

Freddie had been sailing on Victory ships since his graduation from CMA. Their pay rate was not that high, but he had been more interested in getting in the time required to raise his license. That strategy had paid off, as within 18 months of graduation he had enough time aboard ship to sit for his upgrade. His inability to spend money was another benefit of living on a ship where his room, food, and such were included in the job. Now he planned to take the first Second's job that came up, as he was still focused on sailing long and hard to raise his position and eventually earn his Chief's license!

Two years past their graduation, the die was cast for many of Freddie's classmates. Some of those who never went to sea took advantage of a Naval Commission to become a pilot and fly in the Vietnam War air strikes, while others did their military duty before joining the Naval Reserve and taking positions in shoreside companies making various kinds of machinery. Other graduates began to sail, but met ladies who they eventually married, and then stopped going to sea for whatever reason. (Many were convinced that their absence from home was not a good idea.)

However, the majority of the engineering graduates stayed with the program, found their niches, and took on permanent jobs. These were the mainstays of West Coast companies such as Matson, American President Lines, States Line, and Pacific Far East Lines. Some portion of these graduates were also drawn into shoreside work as Port Engineers, especially after they had raised their licenses to qualify for Chief Engineer positions. Again, though, some found a liking for developing their own businesses, stopped going to sea, and were successful in various positions ashore.

Freddie's dream of earning his Chief's license set him on a path which required him to be at sea for as much as ten months of the year to satisfy his Naval Reserve Commission, make a living, and accrue the time necessary to raise his license. He was driven and excited to be learning, traveling, and seeing distant parts of the world which most only read about in books. Freddie was destined to be a marine engineer.

He was also lucky to be in the industry, especially as a marine engineer, as there was a dire need for marine engineers to operate the hundreds of ships supplying the Vietnam War sealift. The other benefit of sailing for months at a time was that Freddie was now a Group 1 member of the MEBA, giving him seniority over the Group 2 members looking for work. He had managed to pay off his initiation fee within his very first year of work.

Due to the many remaining open-board jobs (ones which no one had taken during a previous job call), the MEBA union had two job calls per day, one at 1000 hours and one at 1400 hours. This meant that Freddie had to hang out in San Francisco for pretty much the whole day, and also be prepared to grab his gear and get to a ship as soon as possible. He got a cheap room within walking distance of the union hall and put his mind to the task of getting a job.

Freddie also knew that if he drank too much he might not pass the physical, so he devised a sensible routine: Keep it cool with the drinks at night so he could stay wide awake and have a clear head. Get a good breakfast at the Marine Cooks and Stewards union hall adjacent to the MEBA hall, at 340 Fremont Street, or at the SUP union hall on Harrison Street, a block away from the MEBA hall. Get to the hall 30 minutes before job call, see what jobs were posted, and put his card in if a ship looked good. Wait for the job call. Network with the fellow MEBA union members about ships, crew, and Chief Engineers to learn which ships were good and which ships to avoid if at all possible.

On his first day, the morning call had nothing of interest. In the afternoon, a Second's job came up on one of the Pacific Far East Lines (PFEL) Mariners. These ships were really nice and paid well, with an excellent run to the Orient. Freddie, excited, threw his shipping card in, but the job got snatched up by an old-timer. The man had clearly been waiting for it, as the position was a permanent job and a real plum.

So goes the job call, and the reality of waiting on the beach for weeks or months. Many guys knew when a job was to come up, as a friend would tell them he was getting off for 90 days of vacation or something like that. In the case of the PFEL job, the Second had gotten sick, forcing him to get off and resign his position. All this meant was that Freddie had another day to visit the hangouts in San Francisco and get ready to take a different job the next day.

There is a case of the nerves when you are sitting in the hall trying to get work while paying for a room and anxious to get on a ship. Freddie, mulling this over in his head, realized that he could get a Second's job on a Victory off the open board without any problem. Even so, he really wanted to get some experience on something other than a Victory ship. He could always take a Victory position as a fallback if no other job showed up within the next couple of days. The MEBA dispatcher knew that Freddie had a Second Engineer's license and was always asking him to take one of the Victory ship jobs.

This process went on for another few days, and then the weekend came. He connected with some old classmates and they planned a party at a friend's house for Saturday night. Freddie had no obligations and committed to attending the party, calling up an old girlfriend from his CMA days to see if she was available to go out on Friday or Saturday. He had been celibate for months due to his study and testing routine, with no access to the easy women who were available in the Orient. The connection was made, and the lady was amenable to both Friday and Saturday.

As it turned out the two of them had a lot of fun, since she had just started a job and hadn't been able to go out and party for a while. Freddie made it his mission to entertain her and enjoy himself for the weekend. It might be weeks or months before he could find female companionship once he got on a ship.

Sunday was spent washing clothes and getting a good meal to sober up from the excesses of the weekend. Freddie realized that he had a friends-with-benefits arrangement with the lady of the weekend. She did not appear to be too demanding, and understood that he was a seaman—here for days and gone for months, but while in port he had money and loved to show a girl a good time. Her commitment was minimal, and she actually enjoyed his company as he had great stories of his voyages to Asia.

Monday morning brought the same routine as last week, and Freddie was primed for the job call. He saw the Dispatcher write up the *Azalea City* bound for Vietnam. He had no idea what kind of ship that was except that it was operated by SeaLand and was a container ship. Someone noted it was an old C2 vessel converted years ago and had been running up and down the East Coast for years. None of the other guys looking for a Second's position threw in for the job, though. Not a good sign.

The *Azalea City* C2-S-E1 was a classic design built in 1943 and designated as a "Waterman C2." Her duties as a Naval vessel ended in 1947 when she became owned and operated by Waterman Steamship Company. In 1957, she was converted from a general cargo vessel to a container vessel. The *Azalea City* had an interesting history under SeaLand operations and now she was part of the Vietnam Sealift. Her specifications were as follows:

C2 General Cargo Ship (converted in 1957)
Length: 450 feet
Beam: 72 feet
Draft: 24.9 feet
Speed: 15 knots
Propulsion: Steam turbine
AC-powered steam turbo-generators
Deck Gantry Cranes to allow for self-loading and -unloading (badly needed in the Pacific in 1960s)

Freddie threw in for the job and got the position, along with information on who to call and where to report. The office was in Oakland, as was the ship. SeaLand had realized that containerizing San Francisco was a lost cause, as the railhead required containers to be trucked to a railroad across the bay in Oakland. The San Francisco tunnel to the switching yard by the Cow Palace was too low and small to allow passage of containers, plus the connection to the railroad was all the way down the peninsula by San Jose. For these reasons, Malcolm McLean decided to develop a container port in Oakland across the way from the Oakland Army Terminal. This was the beginning of the end for shipping in San Francisco.

Freddie first paid a visit to the San Francisco clinic to get his physical and shots and whatnot. That took about an hour, and before heading back to his room to pack his gear he made sure to get a bite to eat. The day was likely to be long and the ship was supposed to sail in two days.

When he arrived in Oakland Freddie saw that there were no beautiful lines to the *Azalea City*. The ship had port and starboard sponsons on each side to allow for the installation of gantry cranes on deck. The extension sponsons added room for tracks on which the gantry cranes could move forward and aft along the deck. The unsightly gantry cranes didn't allow the ship a normal profile, since they were stuck up against the forward and aft sides of the house. It was an ugly arrangement, but one which had revolutionized the maritime industry after the *Azalea City's* first sister ship, the *Gateway City*, was built in 1957.

The attraction of containerization was the reduced time and cost of loading and unloading a ship. Prior to the time when container ships were instituted, the cost per ton of loading and unloading a general cargo (break bulk or stick) ship was $5.86 per ton. When the *Gateway City* made her first voyage from New Jersey to Miami in 1957, though, the cost to unload her was just $0.16 per ton. The smart companies realized that they had to change their operation if they were going to survive in the industry.

Freddie was stopped at the gangway by a guard and had to show his paperwork and seaman's documents. When everything checked out, he asked for directions to the Purser's office. Once aboard, the *Azalea City's* appearance remained unsightly; it was a true working ship, without the niceties of new paint to cover the rust streaks running down its sides. Freddie wasn't feeling much more presentable, though. As usual after a physical, he felt kind of crummy from the shots they gave him at the clinic, which often left him with a headache and a fever. He was also packing all his gear in his sea bag, plus his briefcase, so he was sweating like a racehorse.

The Purser was up a couple of decks, and efficiently signed Freddie on before giving him directions to his room and the Chief Engineer's office. As a matter of protocol, the first thing Freddie always did aboard a new ship was visit the Chief. He didn't want to get in trouble by wandering around and having the Chief ask him who the hell he was. As it turned out, this Chief was a nice guy who welcomed him aboard and remarked about Freddie's license being new.

With key in hand, Freddie opened his room, used the head, and took a quick shower. Next stop was the Officer's Mess, as it was dinnertime and he was hungry, his lunch having consisted of a quick sandwich and breakfast not having been all that filling. There the Chief introduced him to the rest of the officers, he shook hands all around, and sat down with the other engineers to eat.

Freddie expected Southern bill of fare, as it was an East Coast ship on which most of the crew were out of the Miami area and had been aboard for a while. He was not too surprised to see a lot of fried foods, greens, and also grits. He ordered a pork chop, greens, and grits. The other engineers began to pump him for information about shipping and what ships he had been on, and the dinner passed quickly.

His one question was about the Seafarers International Union (SIU) Unlicensed crew. Freddie explained that he only had experience with West Coast Unlicensed engine crew who belonged to the Marine Firemen, Oilers, and Watertenders Union (MFOW). His new shipmates set him straight and told him that the SIU Blackgang was committed to the *Azalea City*, all had permanent jobs, and had been aboard for years.

After dinner he changed into his work clothes, grabbed his flashlight, and headed down to the engine room to look around. He wanted to see what he had gotten himself into. The engine room was old, and not as well-cared-for as those of the Victory ships he had sailed on. The boilers were sectional-header types with upper and lower cross drums and four burners fitted in each boiler front. The controls were old Bailey pneumatic controls, and well used. The soot blowers were steam-type, which meant that Freddie's mornings and evenings were going to be busy blowing tubes while under way on his 4 to 8 watch.

He could identify the equipment he saw, and located the particular valves that he needed to use for his job. He pumped the Port Relief Engineer about the ship, and the man filled Freddie in on some issues he had found in his inspection. After an hour and a half, Freddie said goodbye to the Relief guy and headed up to his room. He stopped off at the Officer's Mess to get a cold drink and something to snack on. He was excited yet apprehensive about the ship and knew that his learning curve was going to be a very steep one in the first weeks aboard.

Within 48 hours, they were on sea watches and the ship was set to sail for Vietnam's Cam Ranh Bay. This was the original port used by Malcolm McLean to prove to the US Military that he could containerize the Vietnam War. The *Azalea City's* ability to load and unload herself was vital to this effort, as SeaLand was just getting established in Cam Ranh Bay and there were not yet any cranes on the docks there. This firsthand introduction to not only container shipping but also the great idea of a self-sustaining ship that featured its own crane would come in handy for Freddie.

The trip across the pond (the Pacific Ocean) was normally a long three weeks at about 15 knots on the *Azalea City*. The routine aboard the ship was not unlike what Freddie had been used to on the *Hunter Victory* and *Loyola Victory* ships. The usual noises and smells of the engine room brought back to mind his times aboard other ships, as did the routine of standing watch and eating on a regular schedule with his shipmates.

The difference was that he was now the Second Engineer. As such, Freddie was responsible for the boilers, blowing tubes, testing boiler water, and dosing the boilers to keep their chemistry correct. The first couple of days were somewhat chaotic, as he had to learn his way around the engine room, where all the valves were located, and how to set up the boilers for blowdown and chemical feeding. This required Freddie to be a bit of a chemist, while also watching what was happening to all aspects of the boiler operation to see if adjustments were needed.

Boiler water testing was necessary to maintain the proper chemistry and avoid any internal scale buildup inside the boiler tubes, as well as preventing impurities in the boiler from carrying over into the ship's turbines and auxiliary equipment. The fact that the ship was floating in saltwater (and that sea water was used to cool systems) while the boiler needed to be fed with freshwater featuring a specific salinity and pH meant that Freddie had to check the chemistry twice a day on both boilers. The mechanics of testing the water, adding chemicals, and blowing down the boilers were soon second nature.

Testing the Water/Adding Chemicals/Blowing Down the Boilers:
- The testing chemicals were part of the package bought from the shoreside company which did baseline testing of the boilers while the ship was in port. The procedures were the same as those Freddie had learned at CMA, and the chemical company testing procedures were available to fill in the details. The basics involved making sure that the boilers were properly treated chemically and watching that the boiler feedwater makeup was of good quality. Freddie also had the option of blowing down the water in the boilers if any of the tests were beyond the maximum allowable level.
- Salinity testing was necessary to determine if any seawater might be leaking into the boiler water feed system. If the boilers became too salty these impurities could carry over into the turbines in the main engine and generators. If the test indicated high salinity, then Freddie had to blow down the boilers. The contamination location might be any one of a number of heat exchangers

where seawater was the coolant and the medium being cooled was steam or hot water.

- The purpose of pH testing was to ensure the water remained as neutral as possible, since if it grew too acidic or basic (caustic) this could cause problems with the boiler internals. So long as the proper chemistry was maintained, no scale would build up inside the tubes in the boilers. Since the desalinated water was slightly acidic, it was treated with a caustic chemical to bring the reading to the desired mid-level. (The pH scale measures how acidic or basic a substance is on a scale of 0 to 14, with 7 being neutral. A pH of less than 7 indicates an acid, whereas a pH greater than 7 indicates a base.) The goal was to keep the water close to neutral. If the pH got too high, then the boiler had to be blown down to reduce the number and avoid allowing buildup to form on the inside of the boiler tubes.

- Whenever tests showed the boiler water chemistry was off, the proper chemicals had to be added to neutralize the system and counteract the bad readings. This chemical concoction was poured into a boiler compound tank, which was then closed up and valved to direct the chemical into a specific boiler using boiler feed pressure greater than the pressure in the boilers themselves. One had to leave the boiler compound running to the boiler for a good hour, then wait another hour or so and test again.

- Blowing down the boilers was accomplished using either the upper or lower blowdown lines. Some small lines could be used for what was called a "constant blow." This was done over a period of hours until the chemistry test showed the boiler water was free of the negative readings. The larger bottom blowdown line was more complicated, requiring the boiler to be shut down and valves arranged to use the force of the boiler pressure (440 psi) to push one gauge glass full of water at a time from the boiler over the side. The other blowdown, on the top drum (steam drum), could be used if the water level was too high or if the boiler water was salty and threatening to carry over into the downstream machinery and equipment.

- The other check performed by all the watches was monitoring the salinometer mounted near the throttle platform. This device measured the boiler feedwater and condensate from the main and auxiliary condensers. If the meter showed a high salinity, then the source had to be identified by isolating and testing different systems. This might happen if, for example, a tube in a saltwater-cooled heat exchanger had sprung a leak.

The ship had a long history of operation and had been run hard, as SeaLand kept her busy with their East Coast and Puerto Rico runs. No frills for this old girl, as she was a true working ship recently modified to accommodate the gantry cranes fore and aft. The *Azalea City* had also been fitted with cell guides in the hatches, which allowed for containers instead of the old general cargo open-hatch type arrangement. The boilers had been operated by Second Engineers just like Freddie. Some had been old-time professional Second Engineers who loved boiler work, but some had clearly taken the job for the money and done as little as possible. As a result, Freddie inherited old boilers that needed a lot of tender loving care (TLC).

The Chief Engineer and First made it clear that he could have overtime to clean up the boilers and get the soot blowers fixed and working properly while he was aboard. The limit would be Freddie's tolerance for working 12 hours or more per day in the sweltering heat as they headed towards the tropics. The engine room temperature, especially behind and on top of the boilers, reached in excess of 100 degrees Fahrenheit at sea. Once they arrived in the tropical area around Vietnam, those temperatures climbed as high as 125 degrees Fahrenheit.

He spent the first two weeks repacking and repairing soot blowers. These were manually operated by the Wipers twice a day, and if the old packing was not renewed it made it hard for those poor souls to pull the chains and make the revolutions necessary to clean the soot off the tubes inside the boiler. Freddie noticed that there were completely outfitted spare soot blower heads in the workshop, so he installed these and then overhauled the ones which he'd removed from the boilers. The Wipers were thrilled, as their job became easier.

The soot blowers were designed to use high-pressure steam and a cam-operated valve turned by long chains pulled from below. When pulled, the round metal cam-fitted device opened the valve into a long steel tube with nozzles aligned to the spaces between tubes inside the boiler. While the Wipers pulled the chains, the Fireman increased the air to the burners to push the freed soot out of the boiler and through the stack to the atmosphere. The routine also required calling the bridge to change course so that the wind would carry the clouds of soot away from the ship. The boiler tubes were blown at 0600 hours and 1800 hours each day at sea.

Freddie lost about five pounds on the run between Oakland and Cam Ranh Bay. Along with repairing the soot blowers, he cleaned up a lot of steam leaks. He knew that his dirtiest job would be water washing the boiler internals while they were docked in Cam Ranh Bay, if time allowed for that type of work. This would require him to shut down a boiler, crawl inside, and wash off the soot and built-up slag between the tubes which had not been cleaned by the soot blowers. The air pressure gauges indicated that the pressure drop through the boiler was higher than normal, which indicated that some passages in the boiler were partially blocked.

Arrival and docking Cam Ranh Bay was short and sweet, as it was the foremost deepwater port in South Vietnam. SeaLand was establishing extensive operations there to prove Malcolm McLean's claims regarding the effectiveness of containerizing the Vietnam War. The idea of shoreside cranes to unload and backload empty containers had not yet been realized, though, so there was high demand for ships like the *Azalea City* with the machinery necessary to complete the mission.

The ship was fitted with diesel generators to provide power for refrigerated containers of fruit, meat, vegetables, and such for the troops in Vietnam. At the US port where the container was loaded, each container was connected to a trailer and towed by an independent trucker to the container yard. The yard directed the trucker as to where to leave the container. Then, when the ship was alongside the loading dock, shore cranes or ship's cranes would lift the container from the dock and place it in the correct location aboard ship. At the ship's destination port this procedure was reversed, and once the container hit the dock it was delivered to the receiving location to be opened and emptied.

The port stay in Cam Ranh Bay only allowed for four days to unload the full containers from the ship and backload empty containers to be returned to the States. This process could actually have been done even more quickly, since the gantry cranes could move 15 containers or more per hour, but there were a limited number of SeaLand trucks and trailers on hand.

The ship had scheduled more stops on the way back home to pick up cargo from other Asian ports. Freddie's time off was limited, though, as he was busy in most ports trying to finish various shutdown jobs on the boilers. There would be no twelve-hour time-off bar-hopping on this ship, and he learned that being the Second Engineer was a killer job that was not really to his liking.

If he could just get six months on his Second Engineer's license, though, Freddie could qualify for a temporary First Engineer's license. After their arrival in Cam Ranh Bay he was notified that the permanent Second would not be returning for at least four months due to a medical condition. Freddie was not 100% sure that he could manage six months aboard, but felt he needed the time to get that temporary First License. He also had to satisfy his commitment to his US Navy Commission, which required that he ship ten months a year to prevent him from being drafted into the military.

The water washing of the port boiler in Cam Ranh Bay took a long 12 hours, during which he had to crawl inside the boiler. Freddie discovered that certain locations in the boiler had soot buildup, and it took a lot of work to break up the blockage and use high-pressure water to flush the rest out. Once he found the blockage, he knocked the soot loose with spray and rod, busted out the carbon, and then dried out the boiler and reassembled the entry points. Freddie also had refractory damage to work on before he was finished.

Fortunately he had three Wipers to help him, and they worked as hard or harder than he did. They were as covered with soot as he was, and pulled their weight pumping out sooty water and helping with opening and closing entry points, plus cleaning up the mess. Both Freddie and the Wipers were paid "dirty work" penalty pay for the water washing of the boiler internals. Freddie then spent another two hours steaming the boiler up and drying it out slowly. The actual firing of the boiler to operating pressure would be done by himself, the First, and the other engineers on watch before the ship sailed.

The reality of the hard work required to keep the boilers at peak operating condition hit home as Freddie realized he had one more boiler to water wash before the trip was over. The reason the boilers built up soot on their internal passages was the fuel being burned. Bunker C fuel was one step up from road tar, and had to be heated and then atomized with a burner to combust in the boiler's furnace. Due to the fact that the Bunker C was poor quality fuel and difficult to burn efficiently and completely, the hot soot-forming gases would plate out on the tubes inside the boilers.

MARINE BOILER INTERNALS
CROSSDRUM - SECTIONAL HEADER
TYPICAL ON VICTORY & C2

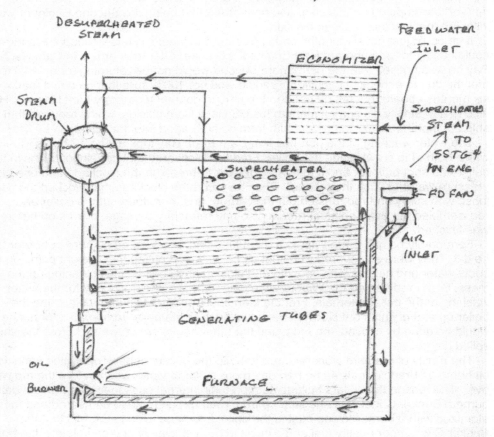

DESUPERHEATED STEAM

FEEDWATER INLET

ECONOMIZER

STEAM DRUM

SUPERHEATED STEAM TO SSTG & MN ENG

SUPERHEATER

FD FAN

AIR INLET

GENERATING TUBES

OIL BURNER

FURNACE

The trip from Cam Ranh Bay to Kaohsiung in Taiwan took seven days of economy steaming and maneuvering around a storm. Freddie's vision of getting off to enjoy a cold beer and perhaps some girl time was not to be, as he was assigned the job of taking on bunkers with the Chief Engineer. This meant that he would be spending hours sounding tanks and opening and closing valves to fuel tanks, plus he had another boiler to water wash.

As it turned out, the ship had to lay off Kaohsiung for part of a day to wait for a berth where they could dock. The bunker barge was to be at the ship as soon as she was docked, and cargo operations would be halted by the port as long as the ship was taking on fuel.

The reason Freddie was responsible for taking on bunkers was that part of his job as Second was to pump fuel (bunkers) from the storage tanks to the settling tanks which fed the boilers. Since he was familiar with the tanks' piping and valve arrangements, the Chief Engineer relied on his assistance to complete the job safely and smoothly.

The ship approached the berth right after Freddie got off watch at 0800. He went to the mess hall to get fed, and prepared to spend the next few hours taking on bunkers. He had already been up for five hours at this point and probably wouldn't get any time off until he finished taking on bunkers, plus standing his watch that night until 2000 hours. By that time he would be bushed, and in desperate need of a shower and bed.

As they started in on the work, Freddie discovered that the Chief Engineer knew the ship well and had begun filling the tanks without having Freddie sound them to see if they were full. (The Chief had used the Wipers and one of the Third Engineers to sound the tanks that they were to fill before they arrived at the dock.) He taught Freddie his method of watching the "static line" pressure (the pressure between the barge's pressure and the tank-valves opened to receive bunkers). By monitoring that pressure and the number of valves opened to tanks on the ship, they were able to determine which tanks were full and needed to be closed. The routine was that if a tank was full, you could close its valve and this would not make a difference in the static pressure. However, if you opened a valve to a tank that was not full then the static pressure would drop.

Freddie still had to take readings on all the tanks after the bunkering to help the Chief determine the amount they had received, and compare the results with the amount the barge claimed they had pumped aboard the ship. The Chief also reminded Freddie to take a drag off the bottom of the settlers after the ship was at sea, in case the bunker barge had water in their tanks. It was common practice in those days to pump a certain amount of liquid off the bottom of the settlers (low suction versus high suction) over the side (into the ocean). This might be anywhere from 50 to 100 gallons each time Freddie performed this maintenance. This practice would be outlawed later in his career, when it became an environmental issue to pump or dump any liquids or solids into the ocean.

The whole process took the better part of the day, and they finished up around the same time that Freddie had to go back on watch at 1600 hours. The Chief sent the same Third out with the Wiper to sound the tanks which had received fuel. Freddie took a quick shower, changed clothes, and went below to relieve the 12–4 Third Engineer. At 1700, the same Third relieved him for dinner so Freddie could eat.

Freddie was back in the engine room by 1720 hours and spent the rest of the watch taking the head off the tanks which the Chief had determined were too full. Freddie filled the settlers, wrapping up a little before he finished his watch. The ship was to stay for two days, so port watches started at midnight and Freddie got to sleep in until the morning since his watch in port was 0800 to 1600 hours. He intended to take it slow, and hopefully get off the ship to decompress a little after more than five weeks spent aboard without going ashore.

All the bars and girls in Kaohsiung were located by the Marine Gate, a very colorful stone arch-shaped structure where the launches landed. The area included the Seaman's Club, bars, restaurants, and such. The US military had a presence there during the Vietnam War period, at which point the country was also under curfew and martial law. Taiwanese military soldiers patrolled the city, marching in groups of three with chromed helmets. The night curfew ran from 0000 hours (midnight) until 0600 hours, and all the bar girls were scared of being caught on the street during that time. The only options were to stay in a bar, get a room, be at the Gate to catch the launch, or be thrown in jail.

Freddie was anxious to be ashore, have a few drinks, and perhaps get lucky and find a girl to share some time with. In the end, though, he was too tired to do much more than grab a meal and visit George's book shop opposite the hotel to see if there were any references on the boilers he was now responsible for. He stopped at the Seaman's club to sit down and have a cold beer, then walked up the street and found a place to get a plate of noodles and some fresh shrimp. There were girls around, and some stopped by to talk to him. He bought rounds of drinks for the girls, and food if they were hungry. He even bought drinks for some of his shipmates. None of the girls caught his eye, though, so he was back at the launch dock by ten at night.

The ride to the ship was a gentle but noisy run to the area where the ship was located. Freddie nodded off and had to be woken up by the driver so he could jump off. The short walk to the ship was quick, and he was up the gangway, into his focsle, and asleep in about 15 minutes. He knew he still had a full day of work ahead of him.

When the Oiler tapped on his door and flicked on his light at about 0700 hours, the man remarked that it was raining and the ship was to leave the next day at 0600 hours. Freddie got up, and took a quick shower to freshen up and get ready for breakfast and his watch, which was from 0800 to 1600 hours. He was in the engine room to relieve the 12–4 Third Engineer at 0745. They talked for a few moments before the Third left to eat, and probably go to bed.

Freddie had bought a textbook about the boilers and intended to see what was inside and what he might learn that could help with his job as Second. The normal routine of testing the boiler water, blowing down the boilers, and such went by quickly, and by 1100 hours he was done. After that he had a quick cup of coffee and sat down to talk with the Oiler about the town, sea stories of past days, and all the drinking he had done and all the women he had met.

The time to go ashore had passed, and as he had to be on watch by 0345 Freddie decided to get a quick meal after he got off watch before returning to his focsle, doing some reading, and heading to bed early. The ship was still being offloaded and backloaded with more empty containers to take to the US. The First and the Electrician seemed to be up 24 hours a day working on the gantry cranes. These were a real creation, and were entirely self-contained as far as the power needed to operate the spreader and such. The diesel generator in the engine room supplied power to the electric motors which ran the gantry cranes forward and aft, along with power for the refrigerated containers aboard. The design required a lot of maintenance, and if it was ever operated incorrectly they would need a significant period of time to overhaul or repair components.

The cranes were designed so that they could be positioned above containers stacked on top of each other. While being carried in the hatches or on top of the hatch covers, the containers in these stacks were locked together using interconnecting box connector (IBC) devices. The crane could move forward and aft, powered by electrical motors controlled by an operator who sat in a cab situated on the spreader which straddled the container to be lifted.

The spreader had an engine room with a Jimmy 6-71 diesel, which operated the spreader via a clutching system, and a small Perkins diesel, which operated the electrical generator for the controls, lights, and such. The driver rode on the spreader, guiding it up and down, fore and aft, and port to starboard with whatever container it was connected to. When the spreader was dropped on top of a container, twist locks were operated to engage the container's four corners. The big diesel was then relied upon to lift the spreader and container either off the ship or onto the ship.

Finesse was required to save the clutch, since a driver who overworked the spreader operation could cause it to slip and burn up. The less talented drivers would keep a heavy load moving slowly, which wore out the clutch faster than lifting it smartly up and down. The arrangement of the operating cab on the spreader put the driver at risk of crashing (marrying) the spreader into the gantry frame if he did not understand and respect the limits of speed and distance involved. The ability to load from the pier was enabled by extensions on the port and starboard sides of the gantry crane frame. These were manually moved from the stowed position when at sea and when in port moved over the side of the ship allow the spreader to move over the dock and pick up or drop off containers.

Freddie was interested in this operation, and his experience on the *Azalea City* would prove to be helpful later in his career when he sailed on American President Lines container ships with gantry cranes. He didn't have much free time to get involved with the loading and unloading process, but managed to discuss the operation and observe its components, both when they were in port and while maintenance was being done at sea. It was an ingenious arrangement, all the moreso for having been fitted aboard a ship with minimal electrical power generating capacity with which to operate large deck machinery.

Imagine sitting in a seat on one end of a cable-driven spreader weighing over two tons, and moving up and down while attached to a SeaLand container weighing up to 15 tons. The start of the upward movement would bring a roar from the big 6-71 diesel, with black smoke pouring from the exhaust. Dropping on top of a container would bring a jolt, and then with a flick of a switch you'd be connected to the container's corners, ready to lift it from the dock to the ship or vice versa.

The cargo operations were pretty steady. Fortunately, the Deck First Engineer and Electrician had done a good job of preparing for the moves, and the drivers had been good and avoided overworking the clutch, which was the biggest maintenance item. The work wrapped up with the backloading of a number of empty containers to be delivered to the US for reloading and shipping back to the Orient.

When Freddie got on watch at 0345 hours the next day, the First Engineer was already in the engine room getting the plant set up for the departure. Vacuum had been left on the main condenser, and the only remaining preparations were to put steam on the engine and test the engine, telegraph, steering gear, and emergency generator, which the First did at each arrival and departure. The Chief would be in the engine room before the first bell was rung down from the bridge. The one-hour notice was when the bridge started the telegraph testing. After that the First left to go test the emergency generator, then swung by the steering engine room to test the steering gear, and also looked over the stern to make sure that no launch or debris was in the way of the propeller.

The port was well equipped with tugs, which assisted the ship in getting away from the dock and turning 180 degrees to head back towards the departure channel. Freddie was at the throttle, and answered all the bells by opening and closing the ahead or astern throttles. The Oiler answered the telegraph and called out the orders coming down to ensure that Freddie knew what direction and speed were required. The Oiler then made the notation in the Bell Book for the time and command from the bridge. The transit from the dock to the sea took a while, as the ship had docked some distance from the departure and arrival channel.

By 0900 hours the ship was taking departure, and the Captain called up the engine room to request 80 rpm. The Chief took the call, and the First and 12–4 Third began to swing valves, shutting off the astern guarding valve and opening the ahead throttle to get 80 rpm. Once the speed had reached 80 rpm and the pressures and temperatures had settled down, they opened up the bleed steam valves on the HP and LP turbines, making sure that the live steam reducing station valves were not also supplying steam to the same system. By then, having spent 12 of the last 24 hours standing watch, Freddie was back in his bunk and fast asleep.

SEALAND SHIPBOARD GANTRY CRANE

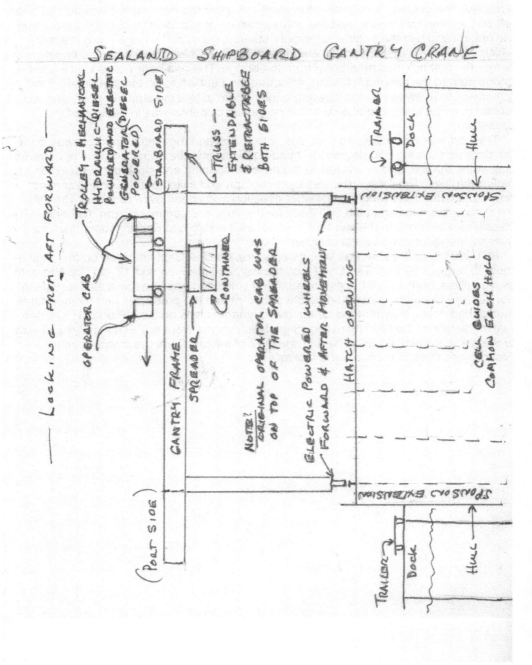

— Looking from Aft Forward —

Trolley — Mechanical Hydraulic (Diesel Powered) and Electric Generator (Diesel Powered)

(Starboard Side)

Truss — extendable & retractable both sides

Operator Cab

Gantry Frame

Spreader

Container

Note: Original operator cab was on top of the spreader

Electric Powered Wheels Forward & After Movement

Hatch Opening

Cell Guides Common Each Hold

(Port Side)

Sponson Extension

Sponson Extension

Trailer

Dock

Hull

Trailer

Dock

Hull

The almost two-week transit from Kaohsiung to Oakland fell into a routine of work, sleep, and eating three squares. For Freddie this involved a welcome four-hour watch followed by overtime in the morning and then sleeping in the afternoon, unless a job came up which required him to work after lunch before he resumed watch at 1600 hours. By this point he had pretty much decided that he did not have the mentality to be a professional Second Assistant Engineer. He wanted more of a challenge and was determined to raise his license as soon as possible. Freddie decided to take advantage of the opportunity to get more time on his Second Assistant license on the *Azalea City* and accept the next trip that was offered to him.

They arrived in San Francisco and pulled up to the Oakland SeaLand pier on a warm spring day in the late afternoon. It was good to see the Sunset and Richmond districts of San Francisco, along with the Golden Gate Bridge, and a little fog was rolling in as they took arrival and took on the Pilot. Transit between the Golden Gate Bridge and the Oakland SeaLand docks was quick, and pretty soon the tugs were pushing the ship against the dock while Freddie managed the throttles and discussed the plant with the Chief and the First. They seemed to like him and approved of his work.

The whole trip had taken about two and a half months, so his payoff was pretty good. He had sent some of his pay to his bank account using a monthly allotment, and the rest was paid off as usual in $100 bills. He kept out about $400, put the rest in an envelope, and asked the Captain to put the envelope in his safe, saying that he would get it when he signed off after the next trip.

The stay in Oakland was to be about one week. A shore gang was aboard for repairs which the Chief and First had requested, including some repairs to the gantry crane. Freddie hoped that he'd have some spare time to entertain his friend-with-benefits girl this visit, and called her to ask if she had any free nights in the next couple of days.

The week went by fast, with work each day, time off each night to visit with his old school chums, and also a couple of nights with his lady friend, Cindy. She adored him for his frank attitude and non-possessive nature as they went to movies, enjoyed good dinners, and spent quality time at night in her apartment. The other evenings were spent with his pals over great Italian meals and reasonable drinks at Original Joe's on Taylor Street in the Tenderloin. By the end of the week, Freddie was actually looking forward to going back to sea instead of eating heavy meals late and drinking a lot of alcohol. He realized that he did not miss the alcohol while aboard ship and at sea.

As a marine engineer, getting on a ship and getting off a ship involve two very different attitudes. When taking on a new job, the Blackgang engineer has probably been on the beach for weeks or months, his bank account is skinny, and he is taking on a job on a new ship which he has no experience on. His mindset is one of fear and apprehension for a week or more, until the reality of operating the steam plant is mastered. By then the seaman is also making money and not having to worry about going broke. After spending months aboard the ship, the marine engineer's confidence level is amazingly high due to the fact that he has weathered many challenges, kept the ship running, been paid off in $100 bills, and refilled his bank account. Psychologically, he has transcended from being nervous and unsure of himself to being settled and cocksure of himself, with money in his pocket.

SeaLand had started to develop container operations in Saigon, Quy Nhon, and Da Nang in addition to Cam Ranh Bay. They had loaded containers for Cam Ranh Bay and Da Nang, so the next trip would be a bit longer than the first one. Once they were back at sea Freddie was synched in, the days seemed to fly by, and pretty soon they were heading back home to Oakland.

At the time, self-contained vessels like the *Azalea City* were still required due to the lack of shoreside cranes in most of the Vietnamese ports. Freddie had come to realize, though, that the days of Victory ships and other break bulk cargo vessels were limited, and pretty soon the only companies that would manage to survive would be those which modified or built new container ships. The Victory ships would soon be laid up again.

The impending demise of break bulk ships was pretty evident to Freddie after being aboard a self-contained ship such as the *Azalea City*. The ship was not as pretty or streamlined as the white ships of States Line, or the Mariners that Pacific Far East Lines maintained. Both of those companies, though, were unable to compete with the container ships which, in just a short amount of time, had proven in Vietnam that they could handle large volumes of cargo more efficiently, loading and unloading in less time and with a much smaller longshoreman labor force. As a result, States Line and Pacific Far East Lines would eventually go bankrupt and cease to operate. Both companies tried to compete using other designs, such as Roll On-Roll Off (Ro-Ro) ships and huge barge-carrying Lighter Aboard Ship Handling (LASH) systems, but none could match the lower labor rates for cargo handling and the speed of loading and unloading offered by container ships.

Freddie signed off, receiving a big payoff and retrieving the envelope with his previous pay from the Captain's safe. The Captain told him to come back anytime, and the Chief and the First were also very kind in their critique of his performance. He had not missed a day of work and made good progress in cleaning up the boilers and soot blowers.

When he walked off the ship, Freddie immediately caught a cab to his bank in San Francisco and deposited his payoffs. His account had grown, and he knew he had to get more time to raise his license so as to earn and save more money. After banking his money, he got another cab to the Gates Hotel on Ellis Street, by the Tenderloin, where the MEBA marine engineers stayed.

He was living a comfortable lifestyle, and was totally focused on raising his license to Chief Engineer. The months aboard ships traveling across the Pacific to and from Vietnam and other Asian ports were not a hardship. Freddie realized that as a single man he had many options, and he was content with the restrictions and commitment involved in working aboard ship and being a part-time resident of the US.

He knew that he was capable of earning his Chief Engineer's license. He also knew, by some inner feeling, that he could eventually take a new ship out of the building yard. The goals which had seemed like fantasies when he graduated from CMA seemed more attainable now that Freddie had been sailing for years as a marine engineer. The idea of being on a brand-new ship as Chief Engineer was still beyond his grasp for the present, though, and would require more sea time and experience aboard a ship as a

Chief Engineer. He knew it was attainable, but he also knew that it would require him to focus, work hard, and prove his capabilities and talents to others.

The Vietnamese ports which Freddie had visited numerous times became like a series of second homes. He was interested in the Buddhist religion, and visited temples to observe how the locals prayed. In the street he was passed by young Vietnamese girls racing along on their bicycles, hair flying back in the breeze. Arrayed in black pants and white tops with long tails, which streamed out behind them, they seemed so gentle compared to the war still in progress just miles away.

US GIs were present, too, with an entirely different appearance and demeanor than the local young people. Many times, Freddie replayed his discussion with a pilot on the Saigon River. The man had said that war had been conducted by the French in Vietnam for 20 years, and that the Americans would be there just as long. The thought sat heavily on Freddie each time he visited Vietnam aboard a ship. He felt very lucky not to have been drafted and become one of the GIs living day to day as part of something which appeared to have no end in sight.

Freddie decided upon a quick dinner and a couple of drinks at Original Joe's on Taylor Street, and then a night's sleep without having to get up a 4:00am (0400 hours). He was tired and did not want to get into a drink-fest with a bunch of people. The owner, who was an old-timer and the bartender, set him up with a cold draft beer and asked if he wanted to eat at the bar. Freddie asked for some chicken scallopini, garlic bread, and another beer. He was set for the next hour just sitting and enjoying the semi-quiet environment, with the television distracting his attention every now and then.

The next day was spent getting his shipping card at the MEBA union hall at 340 Fremont Street in San Francisco. He also had to get some dental work done, and found a dentist through the union who was in the City on Sutter Street. He walked up to the dental office from the union hall and had his teeth cleaned and checked. He had developed receding gums, so another appointment was made for him to be treated for that the next week.

After he finished at the dentist Freddie walked to the US Coast Guard licensing office, which was in the Customs Building on Battery Street. He wanted to know the procedure for getting a temporary First Assistant Engineer's license. He already had more than six months on his Second Assistant Engineer's license. That was an easy process as the Secretary, who had been there forever and remembered him from his last test, gave him the paperwork and list of documents which were needed to get his temporary First license.

This was a new development, as the government realized that they needed upper licenses to fill the slots in the ships anchored in the bay waiting for crew. Finding a Third or Second Engineer was not too much of a problem. Finding a First or a Chief was more difficult, though, so they had decided to allow individuals to sail for six months and then apply for a higher-rated license. This meant that Freddie would not have to climb into boilers anymore, and could start sailing on a ship as its First Engineer.

The very next day, Freddie took all his licenses and discharges from all his ships and went back to the US Coast Guard office to apply for his temporary First Assistant Engineer's license. The whole process took about an hour, and once it was over he could return in two days to get his new license. The two days felt like weeks, as Freddie badly wanted to get back on a ship and get more sea time, now as a First Engineer. He knew that getting a First Engineer's job out of the MEBA Union Hall might require some waiting, though, as his shipping card was not that old.

Finally the whole process of getting his waiver to sail as First Engineer while only having a Second Engineer's license was completed, and he now had a new license which would allow him to sail as a First Engineer. He made it to the Union Hall early to see what jobs were on the open board, hoping that one of them might be a First's job.

As had been the case for the last couple of years, there were Victory ships at anchor waiting for crew. The attraction of sailing on an old Victory ship had lost its luster, and most of the MEBA engineers were looking for something a bit more refined, with higher pay and better accommodations such as air conditioning. The pay rate was still based upon horsepower-tonnage, so the larger the ship and the more cargo it could haul plus the power of its engine determined the pay rate for the MEBA engineers. For example, the Victory ships had only 6,000 shaft horsepower and were designed with approximately 15,200 deadweight tons. New ships with air conditioning and such might have 20,000 shaft horsepower and be rated at 25,000 deadweight tons. The pay rate for the former was considerably lower than that for a new ship with more horsepower and tonnage. The balance, if there was one, was the war bonus and ammunition-carrying bonus for the Victory ships that sailed in the war zone of Vietnam.

Freddie developed his usual routine, finding a cheap room within walking distance of the Union Hall. Most mornings involved an early breakfast at either the Marine Cooks and Stewards Union Hall adjacent to the MEBA Union Hall or at the Sailors Union of the Pacific (SUP) Union Hall around the block. He ran into some classmates who were looking for work, and also some old shipmates from the *Hope Victory* and *Loyola Victory*. Most of them were content to take a five- or six-month job and then sit on the beach for months with their girlfriend or family. Few of the guys were sailing as steadily as Freddie or had the desire to raise their licenses as quickly as he was.

There were two First Engineer jobs on the open board. They were on some East Coast-operated Victory ships that, word had it, were not well run, were bad feeders, or both. Freddie decided to wait for a SeaLand container ship since their pay and overtime were better, they were AC-powered, and they had air conditioning. He had put in almost two years on Victory ships and was tired of going without air conditioning on ships set up with shared showers and toilets. What he was looking for was a ship that was going to give him more experience with containers and gantry cranes. He was also looking for a ship that had a little more comfort than the Victory ships and the old C2 *Azalea City*. In this case, more comfort meant having his own bathroom and an air-conditioned room for the high temperatures and humidity in the tropics.

After a few days Freddie started getting nervous, and he began looking at the Victory ships that needed a First. Freddie learned from talking to his fellow engineers in the hall that most of the open board Victory jobs were on East Coast ships that were not very well maintained. The Dispatcher was trying to get him to take one of those jobs, as there were few licensed First Engineers in the hall looking for a job. Freddie decided that if he could not get a job as First on a SeaLand container ship within two weeks he might be forced to take one of the open board jobs on a Victory ship.

His patience paid off, though, as the SeaLand *SS Los Angeles* relief Engine First Engineer job came up on the board. (SeaLand ships had two First Engineers: Engine, for engine room work, and Deck, for deck work involving the crane and containers.) The permanent Engine First was getting off to have some surgery and would be off for at least five months, maybe more. Freddie threw in for the job, but noticed that no other cards had been submitted.

Asking around, he heard that word was the Chief Engineer was a hard case, and the Engine Room First job was more demanding and paid less than the Deck First Engineer. The Engine Room First did the traditional work of running the Blackgang, maneuvering, and maintenance all over the ship. The Deck First was 100% dedicated to working on the gantry crane and performing maintenance on the refrigerated containers on deck. The Deck First was a plum job, with a lot of overtime due to the necessary rounds on the containers at night and call-outs to handle repairs when the refrigerated containers were not working correctly.

When the relief job for the Engine First Engineer on the *Los Angeles* was called, Freddie got the position. It was an old T3-tanker conversion that had been "jumboized" and converted into a container ship, with a gantry crane to handle its own loading and unloading. The ship was not that old since it was converted, and SeaLand had a policy of keeping their ships running as they had won an award from the US government to "containerize" the Vietnam war.

Having just completed a job on the *Azalea City*, Freddie was familiar with where the office was and who the office people were. He paid off his room and packed his gear after getting his physical and paperwork at the Union Hall. Hailing a cab, he headed across the Bay Bridge to the Oakland Outer Harbor, where the *SS Los Angeles* was berthed.

Freddie wasn't as surprised by his first look at the *Los Angeles* as he had been by the *Azalea City*. It was a converted T3 tanker that had a midsection inserted and a gantry crane installed to handle cargo on and off the ship. The hull and the house had been modified to accommodate the gantry crane rails on the deck. The gantry crane itself was a proven arrangement similar to the one installed on the *SS Azalea City*. The ship was a working ship, and did not have the streamlined body of the break bulk ships which had been the accepted design for handling cargo prior to the 1960s and the Vietnam War.

As noted previously, SeaLand had landed a contract with the US government to containerize the Vietnam War. Accordingly, SeaLand needed ships such as the *Azalea City* and *Los Angeles* to guarantee the company could fulfill its commitments, as there were few (if any) shoreside cranes to load and unload containers. With its own gantry crane, the ship could dock at any port to load and unload containers. The SeaLand program would ultimately manage to deliver 1,200 containers a month to Vietnam to support the war.

After checking into the SeaLand office it was a quick hello and Freddie was on the bus which transported people from the gate to the ship. He was sweating and a little feverish from the shots he had received during his physical. He was also packing about 75 pounds of stuff in his sea bag, and had to haul it up the gangway in two trips. After stacked his gear at the gangway, he hunted up the Chief Engineer's office.

The Chief turned out to be a black man by the name of Charley. He was huge, and filled the desk and chair that he sat in. Wearing a concerned look on his face, he asked Freddie what he wanted. Freddie introduced himself, handed the Chief his dispatch papers, and waited for the next round of questions, if there were any. He was directed towards the First Engineer's room to get acquainted with the fellow getting off the ship, and asked to sign on with the Purser as soon as possible.

Freddie met the fellow who he was relieving, and they spent a few moments chatting. He learned the guy was to undergo an operation and might not be back for at least two trips, maybe more. He helped Freddie with his gear and then they went to the Purser's office. After Freddie gave the man his license and paperwork, signing on took only a few moments.

By now it was towards the end of lunch time, so they stopped by the Officer's Messroom and sat down to eat and talk a little bit more before the First left the ship. He noted that the Chief was an ok guy, but serious, and wouldn't be too friendly until he was assured that Freddie could handle the job. The Deck First was there, and after being introduced the three spent some time eating and sharing sea stories about SeaLand and ships they had been on.

In conversation, Freddie found out that the Unlicensed crew were part of the Seafarers International Union (SIU) instead of the West Coast union MFOW that Freddie was used to sailing with. The permanent Firsts, both veterans of the SIU, told him that the Blackgang was solid and he had nothing to worry about, especially with Charley as Chief.

Freddie learned that the ship was dedicated to the Vietnam run and was fully loaded with containers to offload in Cam Ranh Bay. The containers included a lot of refrigerated cargo, with perishable food and fresh fruit. The ship's three diesel AC generators supplied power for the containers, and all the associated equipment was maintained and operated by the Deck First Engineer. In times of need, of course, all hands turned to and helped out if there was a breakdown on the gantry crane, refrigerated containers, or any related machinery which the Deck First couldn't handle by himself.

The gantry crane on the ship was similar to the type on the *Azalea City*, and was to be a huge learning experience for Freddie. This early exposure would later be vital to his experience working aboard container vessels. In the 1960s the shoreside facilities for containers in Asian ports were not as developed as they were in the United States. For that reason, ships like the *Los Angeles* were badly needed to self-load and -unload in order to fulfill SeaLand's contract obligations with the US government.

No other company had invested in as many ships which were able to handle containers and work anywhere in the world. Most companies were still handling cargo with deck winches and cranes in the tried and proven break bulk method, though APL, Matson, and US Lines had developed some container-type operations. Shipping containers could be transported to the supplier to be loaded, and then trucked to the pier where the ship was docked. There they would be loaded aboard by either a shoreside crane, the ship's gantry-type crane, or in some cases electro-hydraulic cranes installed aboard ship. This was more secure, less labor intensive, less expensive, and additionally resulted in less cargo theft.

The day was full, and Freddie did not get settled in his focsle until late at night. Before turning in, he made his rounds of the ship and learned the basics of the plant, including the locations of all the valves which he would need to operate when they left for Vietnam within a day or so.

Freddie was in the engine room at 0800 hours the next morning, and noted that the Chief was already there and checking things out. He seemed to be everywhere on the ship, from the engine room to the deck operations to the gantry crane. By word of mouth, Freddie learned that the Chief was a long-term SeaLand employee with a lot of experience on crane ships like the *Azalea City* and *Los Angeles*. It was apparent that he was well thought of by SeaLand and the other old-time Chiefs in the company.

T3 tanker design (such as the *Los Angeles*) prior to conversion to a container ship
Length: 501 feet
Beam: 68 feet
Draft: 29.6 feet
Speed: 15 knots
Gross Tons: 9,880
Propulsion: Steam Turbine – single screw
Shaft Horsepower: 7,700

Within two days Freddie was knee-deep in the operation, and he was at the throttle when the ship departed from the dock in Oakland and headed towards Vietnam. The long voyage to Vietnam provided ample time to perform maintenance on the gantry crane. Within a couple of days Freddie noticed the Chief was on the gantry crane overhauling the clutch system and doing other maintenance in preparation for Vietnam. He was also in the engine room taking on jobs, welding pipe, and such.

One of the Third Engineers was a young guy fresh out of a Maritime Academy who had been on the ship for about six months. He was a gifted welder, which earned him lots of overtime as assigned by the Chief Engineer. The Chief was also in the thick of the operation. The other Third was an old-timer who took the maintenance of the generators in hand. He was gifted, and had sailed with APL as Chief years ago before quitting sailing and starting to work ashore. Recently he had decided to return to the ships, as money was good and he was tired of both the 9 to 5 existence and not having any disposable income. The Second Engineer was a professional Second and loved working on the boilers, which seemed to reflect his competence.

Disaster struck ten days outside of Oakland, as the saltwater evaporator broke down and the plant salted up from a leak in one of the saltwater heat exchangers. This was a really bad set of circumstances as the ship was in the open ocean, running out of freshwater for the boilers, and had no way to generate new freshwater. The Chief started troubleshooting and assigned Freddie to fix the evaporator. The fault was found to be a leaking heat exchanger tube, which could be fixed in a day or so. In the meantime, though, the ship had to maintain speed, so the Chief started using the boilers as evaporators to generate freshwater!

Freddie had never heard of this approach. The Chief told him that they were going to use saltwater to feed the boilers and force-feed chemicals into the system while continuously surface blowing the boilers to prevent any carryover into the plant. Between the Chief and himself, they stood engine room watches with the other engineers to make sure that there was no carryover and that freshwater was being correctly generated by the boilers.

The extra feed of saltwater filled the DC heater with water to be used for the boilers. After a time, the DC heater was dumped to the distillate tanks. The continuous surface blow of the steam drum kept the carryover problem in check. Within a day they had managed to fill up one distillate tank, and the evaporator was back in operation and making boiler water. The Chief had rationed freshwater for the crew for three days, so everyone was getting a bit nasty and needed a shower, but all understood the emergency. The whole approach taken by the Chief was one for the textbooks.

After a week the plant had settled back down and Freddie tried to catch up on some maintenance in the engine room. By this point he had noticed that his foscle room was over the diesel generator room, and the grinding noise of the Jimmy 6-71 engines had become background noise. One night he heard something that felt off in the way the engines sounded and called the Deck First, but found out later that his warning had come too late, and one engine had a bad bearing.

This was a real problem because they had a full load of refrigerated containers which required three operating diesel generators to provide enough power to keep the boxes in temperature. Still, the Deck First was able to manage by shutting off rows of refrigerated containers in turn, so that the two remaining generators could handle the load.

The next night, though, the same off-normal sound occurred, and another generator was lost. The gear train which ran its blower had failed, and the engine had sooted up and stopped. Now they were down to one generator, which was not sufficient to keep all the boxes in temperature. To make matters worse, the ambient temperature was getting hotter. The ship had a whole week left before it would reach Vietnam, and it looked like they could start losing refrigerated cargo.

The Chief, the Deck First, and Freddie sat down and tried to develop a game plan. Some of the refrigerated containers were self-contained and could be run with propane gas to operate a diesel-engine-driven electric generator. The limiting factors on this solution were the number of gas bottles aboard and the number of refrigerated containers which featured self-contained propane diesel-electric generators. It would address part of the problem, though, so the Deck First picked the most critical refrigerated containers to operate independent of the ship's diesel generators.

In conversation, Freddie suggested that they make one good generator out of two broken ones. The engines were fairly simple six-cylinder machines, and their parts were interchangeable. Turning their attention back to the two engines which had failed, they selected the least damaged one and stripped the other of the parts needed to fix the first.

One head had to be cleared of carbon, as the drive for the blowers had seized and filled all the passages with carbon. One good piston, rod, and lower connecting rod bearing were scavenged from the more damaged engine and used to rebuild the one bad cylinder of the engine they were attempting to salvage. The gang pulled together and worked around the clock, and within 24 hours the one engine was reassembled and they were ready to try to start it.

The start-up of the engine was anti-climactic, as it ran and filled the somewhat small diesel generator space with soot and carbon. All those gathered around had smiles on their faces, though, since they knew the ship would not lose any refrigerated cargo. The Chief could be seen through the carbon-filled air with a big grin on his face.

The next step was to synchronize the repaired generator with the one that was carrying the entire electrical load for the refrigerated containers. The Chief and the Deck First managed that, and balanced the load between the two operating generators so they had ample power to feed all the refrigerated containers. This saved the day, as without the second generator there would not have been enough power to keep the refrigerated container boxes in temperature and some refrigerated cargo would have spoiled.

These two unorthodox repairs to the boilers and the diesel generators demonstrate the need for initiative and resourcefulness among Blackgang marine engineers. They operate and repair complex equipment out in the middle of the ocean, without any support from ashore. The Blackgang has to make do with what they have on hand to keep the ship running and ensure its cargo is safe, properly cared for, and delivered to the end user.

The other educational job that Freddie participated in was the care and troubleshooting of the refrigerated containers (reefer boxes). The Deck First was overwhelmed. He had reefer boxes that had not been correctly prepared before being loaded aboard ship, or had "hot" loads which needed to be cooled down and then set at 0 degrees Fahrenheit for fish and beef, or kept at 34 degrees Fahrenheit for vegetables and fruit. Freddie volunteered without being asked to assist. He learned how to manually defrost the reefer boxes, change parts, and troubleshoot the boxes which had frozen up with all the additional moisture and would not maintain the needed temperature.

This again would turn out to be very valuable experience for his future trips on container ships. The most valuable cargo was refrigerated goods such as fruit, fish, and such. For example, surimi (fake crab) is made by the Japanese from Alaskan white fish, and is considered the most valuable reefer cargo aboard a container ship.

The balance of the trip was somewhat uneventful, and the ship prepared for its stay in Cam Ranh Bay, Vietnam. Most of the last few days were spent on the gantry crane, to make sure that it was in good operating shape and capable of running for hours at a time. Much of the wear and tear on the gantry crane came from improper operation by the longshoremen. Sometimes the crew would operate the crane to make sure that it was not overworked or damaged due to being run at excessive speeds at the end of the crane's reach. Damage could also occur during maintenance or set-up on port if the man driving the crane ran the spreader up against the gantry frame too fast and broke the cables. Freddie would witness such an accident in person and take part in the follow-up repairs later in the trip.

After the generator and boiler repairs Freddie could do no wrong, and he and Charley got along quite well. The stay in Cam Ranh Bay went pretty smoothly, and cargo was removed and trucked away to the holding area. The backloading was primarily empty containers, some of which were filled with old or damaged military gear being sent home for repairs. The homebound trip was set with stops in other ports to pick up cargo for delivery to the US so that the ship's cargo space was being utilized and making money. This meant that Freddie might get some time off and get ashore!

The trip home included stops in Kaohsiung and Yokohama to pick up cargo, so the complete amount of time for the first voyage ended up being 85 days. Freddie needed the time on his license, so on the way back home he decided he would stay on for a second voyage. This could give him almost six months aboard the ship, and that meant he would be able to sit for his First Assistant license. He was obligated to sail ten months a year according to his US Naval Reserve Commission, and he also had to take correspondence courses. As it was, Freddie had more than ten months at sea in any one calendar year since he was only spending a month on the beach when he got off a ship and then getting back aboard to sail for four to six months.

In Kaohsiung, the Second Electrician driving the gantry crane was trying to show off for his girlfriend on the dock. Bringing the spreader up too fast, he jammed (two-blocked) it against the gantry crane frame, breaking the supporting cables and dropping the spreader down onto the dock. This meant that Freddie and all the others had to help with repairs taking all of 12 hours.

New cables had to be found and fed through the sheaves and onto the spreader. The spreader had also been damaged, and the Chief directed those repairs while Freddie worked with the Deck First and the Bosun to get the new cables into place. In the end the repairs were completed relatively swiftly, but everyone was exhausted and gave the

Second Electrician the evil eye. The Chief informed him that his services were no longer required, and all expected him to request to leave the ship, take vacation, and never return to the *Los Angeles* once the ship docked in Oakland.

Freddie had found himself a home, and was content to be part of the core group of engineers on the *Los Angeles*. He paid off in Oakland and immediately signed on again when it was announced that the regular Engine First Assistant would not be returning until the following trip. Charley was getting off for vacation, as he had been aboard for two trips and needed to take time off. That made Freddie's willingness to sail another couple of months highly agreeable to Charley and the folks in the SeaLand office. By now Freddie had a firm grasp of container ship and gantry crane operations and maintenance.

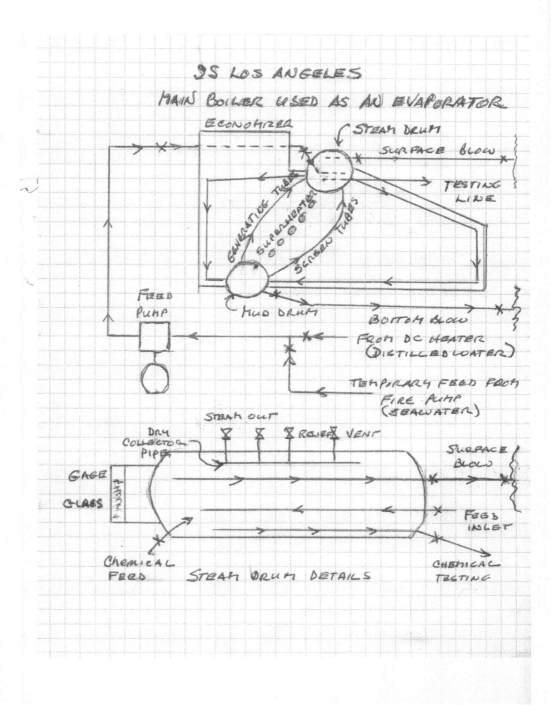

SS LOS ANGELES

MAIN BOILER USED AS AN EVAPORATOR

ECONOMIZER

STEAM DRUM

SURFACE BLOW

TESTING LINE

GENERATIVE TUBES

SUPERHEATER

SCREEN TUBES

FEED PUMP

MUD DRUM

BOTTOM BLOW

FROM DC HEATER (DISTILLED WATER)

TEMPORARY FEED FROM FIRE PUMP (SEAWATER)

STEAM OUT

DRY COLLECTOR PIPE

RELIEF

VENT

SURFACE BLOW

GAGE GLASS

FEED INLET

CHEMICAL FEED

STEAM DRUM DETAILS

CHEMICAL TESTING

SS LOS ANGELES
DIESEL GENERATOR ROOM
MID-TRIP EMERGENCY REPAIRS
(23HR REPAIR JOB)

440VAC GENERATORS

JIMMY 671 DIESELS

□	#2 CLEANED HEAD WAS INSTALLED & DAMAGED PISTON REPLACED FROM #2 — (#3)
□	← FAILED BLOWER GEARS USED HEAD AND ONE PISTON & CONN' ROD FOR #3 — (#2)
□	ONLY GENERATOR OPERABLE — (#1)

SEALAND SHIPBOARD GANTRY CRANE

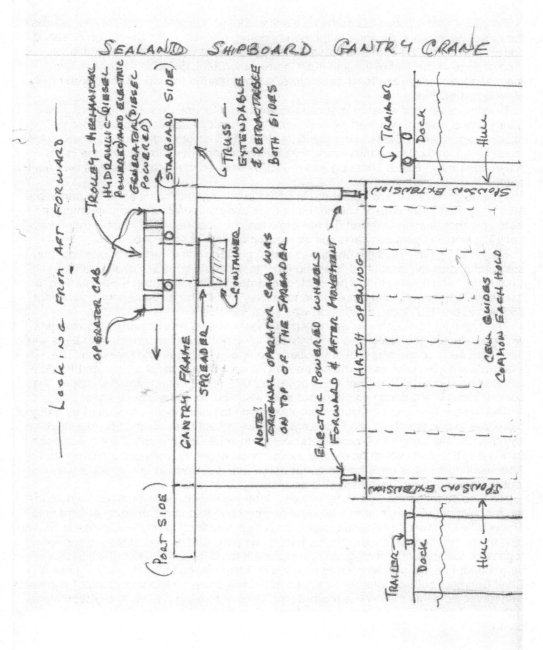

← Looking From Aft Forward

Trolley — Mechanical Hydraulic (Diesel Powered) and Electric Generator (Diesel Powered)

STARBOARD SIDE

Truss — Extendable & Retractable Both Sides

Operator Cab

Container

Gantry Frame

Spreader

Note:
Original operator cab was on top or of the spreader

Electric Powered Wheels Forward & After Movement

Hatch Opening

Cell Guides Co. Know Each Hold

Sponson Extension

Trailer

Dock

Hull

(PORT SIDE)

Sponson Extension

Trailer

Dock

Hull

Freddie's next trip was the same as his first, though fortunately without any failures of the diesel generators, damage to the gantry crane, problems with the boiler, or salted boiler feedwater. Part of this success (or lack of failures) was due to the extensive repairs done at the end of the first trip. Charley, the Chief, called in for repairs and maintenance to all three diesel generators, so they started the trip off with three newly overhauled engines.

Charley developed a better maintenance plan for the vital diesel generators. The gantry crane was not watched as thoroughly as when Charley was aboard, but the repairs performed in Oakland improved its reliability. The other development which took much of the load off the gantry crane was the installation of shoreside cranes in the Asian ports they visited. That upgrade reduced the need to rely on the ship's own gantry crane.

Freddie got a chance to go ashore in both Kaohsiung and Yokohama. He had some favorite spots to visit and, of course, he had his eye out for female companionship as well. The short stay in Oakland did not allow him the opportunity to visit his friend-with-benefits, since he was busy and she was occupied with her new job.

Kaohsiung gave Freddie a chance to add to his library at George's book shop, and the hotel across the street had "dancing girls" to entertain guests. Yokohama had Chinatown, which was still the hot spot for seamen visiting that port. It was starting to get gentrified, though, with more "Japanese Only" bars. The exchange was still about 356 yen to one US dollar, so the port was still affordable.

The highlight of Yokohama was its small guest houses, with soaking tubs and girls who gave massages using their feet by walking up and down your back. The beds were fitted with huge comforters that enveloped one after a hot soak and massage. The elaborate sukiyaki houses on the hill above Chinatown were fit for a king, and Freddie lounged on comfortable pillows while being fed by a female attendant who dipped the cooked items in a raw egg and kept hot sake available for the many courses.

The tedious two week crossing from Yokohama to Oakland was extended by a day or more due to bad weather. The First Engineers were kept busy for the first four days trying to get the refrigerated containers settled down, as the Japanese were notorious for loading hot loads which needed to be defrosted to get the temperatures in range. After working 16-hour days for the better part of the first week at sea, Freddie was looking forward to getting off the ship and having some down time.

His time spent on the *Los Angeles* was a learning experience which put Freddie in the mindset of being able to handle most any problem that might develop aboard ship. The realities of working on a seagoing ship (which functions in many ways like a floating city) out at sea thousands of miles from its home port, with no shoreside support for repairs or maintenance, forced marine engineers to be inventive when the conditions demanded. Freddie also learned to be humble, keep his mouth shut, and not buck a Chief Engineer such as Charley who was 100% hands-on, unlike some Chief Engineers who never went into the engine room. The politics of forming a team and getting along with your shipmates became a creed of sorts that would carry Freddie through his whole career.

SIGNING OFF THE *SS LOS ANGELES*

RAISING HIS LICENSE AND FINDING A SOUL MATE

At the end of the trip, Freddie signed off and took stock of both his bank account and the time on his license to see if he had enough sea-going time to sit for his permanent First Assistant Engineer's License – Unlimited Steam. In his mind he had a full year between the time on his Second Assistant Engineer's license and the time on his Temporary First Assistant Engineer's license. In other words, he had built up the required one year of sea time. He just had to make a trip to verify his credentials and sea time with the US Coast Guard in San Francisco.

He booked a room in San Francisco for a week, rented a car, and partied for about two days with old shipmates and classmates who still lived or worked out of the San Francisco Bay Area. Many of his pals had hooked up with ladies and moved to Santa Cruz, Oregon, or Nevada, but a few of the hardcore sea-going types were still living and working out of San Francisco. Some of these kept a room (crib) in the Tenderloin, where a number of engineers hung their hats at the Gates Hotel on Ellis Street, and many Unlicensed guys stayed at the Olympic Hotel on Eddy Street.

Some of the hotels in the neighborhood even had staff who could introduce ladies to the tenants, so the Tenderloin offered lodging, companionship, food, and bars all wrapped into one. The climate was changing, though, as some Vietnamese were moving into the Tenderloin. The other interesting development was Cecil William's Glide Memorial Church on Ellis and Taylor, where Sunday celebration had first-class music plus a rousing service with feel-good sermons by Cecil.

Freddie's friend-with-benefits lady was available, and this renewed a relationship which he had now been thinking about for some time. Cindy was a San Francisco-born, American-raised Filipina, which had attracted Freddie right off. They seemed to get along and their relationship was open, without pressure from either side.

Freddie had witnessed broken marriages among his own family and friends, and she had suffered the same sort of exposure. As a result, they were both cautious regarding their relationships. Freddie was slowly tiring of living out of a suitcase while off a ship, though, and looking to settle down with some roots. The idea of marriage and a permanent relationship remained unspoken, but not too remote a thought during his time off, and even at times when he was aboard ship.

He still dearly wanted to get his Chief Engineer's license, and had made fast progress toward that goal in the last four years since graduating from CMA. The US Coast Guard agreed that Freddie had adequate time to raise his license. The catch was that he had no time which would go towards his Chief's license, so he would have to sit for his First Assistant Engineer's license and then sail for one year to be eligible to sit for his desired Chief Engineer's license.

Freddie moved to Oakland and got a room close to Law's School of Marine Engineering to prepare for his exams. This was a great resource, as Law had years of data which he had received from ex-students who shared their experiences with Law after sitting for their licenses. The rotating class offered about four to six weeks of instruction for any license you might be studying for. The revolving class made it easy to start at any time and complete at your own pace.

Freddie took advantage of all the class time, and stayed after class for at least two hours or more before leaving for dinner and then heading back to his room to resume studying. Within three weeks he felt confident enough to set a date for his exam. He would be able to start the exam on a Monday with possible completion on Friday, or earlier if he was able.

Law's proved to be right on once again, and Freddie breezed through the exams, finishing up on the third day. He went to the Golden Bull bar-restaurant across the street and had a cold beer and a cheeseburger while waiting for his license to be completed. The beer hit his empty stomach hard, particularly since he'd had no liquor for the three weeks he had been studying at Law's.

Finally Freddie had his First Assistant Engineer's license! He was pumped and excited, and knew that he would be able to get his Chief Engineer's license in a year or a little more. That would give him the credentials to sail as Chief Engineer or pursue other avenues of engineering, and widen his exposure to the world of engineering in other specialties. He recognized that he was very weak in electrical systems and troubleshooting those types of problems on a ship. He was not alone, as most marine engineers shared a similar weakness. Electricity was like the black art and he had to find some way to get better at it during the time he was sailing or perhaps once he got his Chief's license.

He called on his friend-with-benefits and she was available, so he invited her to dress up and join him for dinner in the City. He was thinking that Lew Lehr's Steak House might be nice, perhaps followed by a show or something afterwards. Lew Lehr's was in the Olympic Hotel and was an upscale restaurant with prime cuts of meat. Freddie still had his car, so he picked her up and they headed out for a night on the town.

It was a Friday so they could stay out late without disrupting her routine. She said that she was burnt out from the schedule at work and was looking forward to being spoiled a bit. The dinner was great, and they walked the few blocks to the Golden Gate Theatre to see a newly released movie, which they enjoyed.

As they talked, Freddie learned that she too was looking for some advancement, but since she wasn't able to afford to go to college she thought she might join the Peace Corps. She had a dream of going to college, though she was not sure what she wanted to major in. She had never traveled, and was a great listener when Freddie opened up about his travels to the Orient, especially the Philippines.

Cindy Flores was a one-of-a-kind lady who was unique compared to most to the Stateside women Freddie had dated. The most refreshing part was that she did not get crazy about sex being part of their somewhat open relationship. Freddie had no one else he considered a girlfriend, as his previous attempts had turned out badly.

Cindy was fun and enjoyed his spoiling her for the next week until it came time for him to depart to get more sea time to sit for his Chief Engineer's license. They talked about sharing a rental someplace, and during that week found a location and moved what little stuff they owned into the unit. It all fit in the rental car, which he had kept for this purpose.

Freddie felt a need and desire to help Cindy by footing the better part of the rent, and was glad to help her get ahead since her hairdresser earnings weren't enough to allow for a larger, more comfortable place. They visited estate sales and flea markets and outfitted their San Francisco flat by Dolores Street. Freddie was about as close to settled as he had been for years. He was certainly not inclined to go back to his hometown, as it was filled with too many bad memories.

The next chore was to get a job. Freddie knew this meant he might have to take another Victory ship, since First Assistant jobs rarely came up on the shipping board at the MEBA hall in San Francisco. In the meantime, he established a new kind of routine. His nights were spent with Cindy, who turned out to be a good cook. She introduced Freddie to some Filipino dishes, and their grocery shopping trips ranged from stores specializing in Filipino foods to ones located in Chinatown, where food was fresh and cheaper. In the mornings he would get dressed and drive her to her job, and then he was off to the union hall to look for a job himself. Freddie had to leave some money for Cindy for the apartment and food and such, so he was anxious to get a job to keep his bank account filled.

The third day he was at the hall, he noted a job on the *Long Beach*, a converted C4 SeaLand ship which had no crane. There was a relief job for 90 days that Freddie threw his card in for. He was both anxious and kind of sad at the thought of getting the work and heading back out to sea. As luck would have it, he got the job.

After going through the physical, introducing himself at the office, and getting his gear aboard, he informed the Chief that he had to turn in his car and would be back aboard in the morning. The rest of the day was spent with Cindy tidying up his obligations, leaving her settled, and letting her know where he was going and when he might be able to call.

C4 class vessels were originally the largest cargo ships built by the US Maritime Commission during WWII. The design was initially developed by American-Hawaiian Lines before being taken over in 1941 for the war effort.

Length: 520 feet
Beam: 71.6 feet
Speed: 17 knots
Propulsion: Steam turbine
Shaft Horsepower: 9,900

This vessel (the former *Marine Flasher*) and other sister ships had been bought by SeaLand and converted into container ships between 1964 and 1968 in Pascagoula, Mississippi. All cargo gear was removed, and their holds were converted into container cells with hatch covers designed for deck loading of containers.

The layout of the *SS Long Beach* was very comfortable as SeaLand had completely renovated the house to make it entirely air conditioned, unlike the ships which Freddie had sailed in the last few years. Each room had new furniture, and every crew member had their own focsle. The engineering team included some men he had met on previous ships or in the union hall. The Deck First, a former schoolteacher, had the largest room. This became the meeting and drinking place for both the engineers and the outspoken but talented Chief Electrician who helped the Deck First.

The regular Chief Engineer was off on vacation, and the relief was the normal Engine First Engineer. The Blackgang crew were old-time MEBA engineers and SIU union unlicensed guys who loved the permanent Chief Engineer. He was a real professional, and had spent years aboard ship as Chief in addition to being a shoreside repair specialist. He brought out the best in all his men, and the Blackgang called him "Big Daddy Tom." The engineers were just in love with him due to his expertise and gentle manner. There was no strife or discord, as everyone wanted to work for him and be on his team. They shared the old philosophy of drinking hard, working hard, and turning-to no matter where the problem was.

Freddie filled right in behind a First he had sailed with on a Victory ship, who was of the same genre as Big Daddy. Clyde was a habitual sea-going man with no real ties to life ashore. He lived in a hotel when off the ships, kept no family ties, and drank in excess, but aboard ship he shined and could handle each and every situation as second nature. This meant that Freddie had little or no rebuilding to do. The SIU crew looked to be pretty solid, and the Chief Electrician was the chairman with the Bosun and held the SIU members in check.

The *Long Beach* had no gantry cranes but featured huge diesel generators capable of supporting many refrigerated containers. The engineering plant was a classic C4 design dating back to WWII times. The Blackgang included an Engineer, Oiler, and Fireman on each watch. The Deck First was backed up by a Chief and Assistant Electrician, which removed the need for the Deck First to understand or handle any electrical problems. The run included some ports in Vietnam but was primarily focused on serving the Asian ports of Japan, Korea, Hong Kong, and Taiwan. The ship ran almost flawlessly and allowed for a heavy party environment as someone was always available to help no matter what the problem.

This ship was a prime example of why SeaLand was taking over the runs to Asia via the West Coast. Companies like States Line and Pacific Far East Lines were struggling to keep up with the likes of this kind of operation. APL at least seemed to have caught on with the concept of containerization, and was both converting their break bulk ships and designing their new vessels to serve as container ships.

The old practice of running ships through the Panama Canal to handle cargo to both the East and West Coasts of the US was going away, as rail connections to the East Coast could get cargo from West Coast ports to East Coast distribution destinations faster by putting the shipping containers on rail cars. Such changes led to the demise of the break bulk ships, which also needed huge longshoreman crews to load and unload break bulk cargo. The cost per ton of cargo management for container ships was a small fraction of that for break bulk ships, and the pilferage was less.

Freddie had personally witnessed this in his short tenure as a marine engineer, having trained on a break bulk type ship and also been aboard Victory ships for the first two years of his career at sea. He understood the need and the concept.

At one point he had tried to defend his selection of jobs to a classmate's father who was a States Line Vice President. When asked by the gentleman who he was sailing with, Freddie proudly said, "SeaLand."

The father replied: "Traitor."

Freddie simply answered, "Yeah, but they are making money."

SeaLand was locked into what would become the way of the world, while States Line had hooked their concept to Roll On-Roll Off (Ro-Ro) ships. Their ships were making money in foreign ports but being killed in the US, as their price per ton of loading on the West Coast of the US was more than double of that of SeaLand and other companies who accepted the inevitable containerization. SeaLand could handle about 25 containers per crane per hour when loading and unloading containers. States Line ships had to load and unload cargo using forklifts or by driving trucks or other vehicles on and off the ship, which was time consuming and labor intensive.

The downside to container ships was that the time spent in a foreign port was limited to a maximum of two days, versus five or more on break bulk ships. This changed the port time activity of all crew members, some of whom lived in foreign ports when off a ship or had developed longstanding friendships with vendors and bars catering to seamen. There was even a chance that one's time off could be limited to mere hours, as some time was spoken for to handle repairs that could not be done while underway.

Freddie also noted that the many bars and bar-girls were starting to disappear. This was in part due to the lack of business, but also thanks to the development of a middle class which ended the need for women to participate in the age-old profession. There were now well-paying jobs which hired women, enabling them to support the families and dependents who relied upon them.

Freddie was able to get two trips on the *Long Beach*, which put him almost at the halfway mark towards sitting for his Chief Engineers license. The idea he had formulated to get his Chief's license in five years was looking possible. He recognized, though, that his acceptance into the hard partying *Long Beach* culture was not healthy for him, and that he was starting to fall back into his hard-drinking patterns from his early years in his hometown.

He also realized that he could blow it with his friends-with-benefits lady in San Francisco if he took the road to becoming a hard-drinking seaman. It occurred to him that his early days going to sea had included a lot of heavy drinking while ashore, and that he had probably turned off women who expected some of that kind of behavior, but not a daily diet of it (with all the baggage that included). With this in mind, Freddie decided he would get off the *Long Beach*, dry out ashore, and look for another ship as a First Engineer.

Signing off the *Long Beach* was like leaving a boy's club, which had been the support group for a whirlwind of hard work, hard drinking, and partying. Once off the ship he launched into the normal routine of going to the hall to get a shipping card, putting his payoff in the bank, and then heading to what was now his home with Cindy. How things changed when one committed to having a special lady!

42

She was working when he got back to the apartment, and he noted that the appearance of their living space had metamorphized during his time aboard the *Long Beach*. Cindy had decorated the place, and filled the refrigerator with beer and food for him. Freddie was tired and needed to rest and decompress, so he took a quick shower, had a cold beer, and went to sleep. He was awakened by a fragrance, which he recognized as the floral scent Cindy wore, and turned to see the woman who was the love of his life.

A quick three weeks were absorbed by the lifestyle that Freddie had been looking for, spending time with a loved one and doing simple things to please Cindy. He spoiled her, but she seemed to enjoy the simple things like a dinner at home and taking walks around the City. He backed off on his drinking, and started to jog while she was at work to get back into shape.

While Freddie ran he reflected on his early days, his mother's alcoholic tendencies, and his out-of-control drinking as a young person. He could work hard aboard a ship for months and drink very little, if at all, but once he was not obligated, he still had a tendency to "binge" drink. For the moment, though, he was content to not visit the union hall or go out bar-hopping as he was truly domesticated. Freddie realized that, for the first time in a long time, he was happy and did not need the rush which accompanied being drunk.

His days were more sedate, and he relished being able to take the time to cook a meal for Cindy and prepare her a bath when she got home. He bought a used VW Bug, which allowed them some independence. They used it to venture outside the City, and Freddie also drove Cindy to and from work. They talked about future plans and what might lay ahead. She was in sync with his idea to get his Chief Engineer's license, which was just months away. She also discussed her dream of going to college and learning a new craft beyond hairdressing. Her idea of joining the Peace Corps was fading away.

Rather than worrying about getting a newer ship, Freddie went to the hall and looked for any job as First Engineer. That included looking at positions on Victory ships, plenty of which were anchored in San Francisco Bay and awaiting crew. He would get organized with clothes, new work shoes, and such, then get a job and kill off the last six months needed to qualify for his Chief Engineer's license exam.

The opening he was looking for seemed to appear all too soon. The *Hunter Victory* was to be broken out again after being laid up by MARAD. Freddie knew that he could handle the work, as he had spent nearly two years on Victory ships after he graduated from CMA.

The job call was not well attended, and his card was the only one thrown in for the permanent First Engineer's job on the *Hunter Victory*. After getting the shipping information he noted that the steamship company managing the ship was APL. This was a bonus, as that company was known for its professional shoreside operations department.

Freddie got his physical, picked up his gear at home, and drove to the ship, which was berthed at Hunter's Point Shipyard (a former Navy facility now operated by AAA Machine Shop). The Chief was young and very friendly, and this was his first time serving as Chief Engineer. They synched immediately, and Freddie told him that he needed to pick up his friend at the end of the day but would be aboard first thing in the morning. He had called Cindy to alert her that he had a job and would be picking her up a bit late.

The process of last-night-at-home was a first for Freddie. Things became a bit emotional, so they both stiffed it out and knew that they had a good relationship. Neither wanted to put any burden on the other, and both wanted to allow the opportunity for the other to reach whatever they felt was their destiny. Their quick dinner out and quiet evening together were warm and friendly.

He had left enough money to cover his part of the rent and other support that he felt obligated to provide. She had an apartment, a VW Bug, a job, and a sometimes-home marine engineer. He told her that he thought the ship might allow him to get his needed six months to sit for his Chief's license, but it would probably mean at least two trips on the *Hunter Victory*. She smiled and told him she would drive him to the ship.

Freddie was aboard, dressed, and in the Officer's Mess by 0700 hours. The Chief greeted him and told him that the Second was taking over the watch from the MEBA Relief Engineer who had stood the night watch. They had some time to eat breakfast and discuss what needed to be done to get the ship ready for sea.

The Chief had been aboard while the *Hunter Victory* had been steamed up and broken out of the layup fleet at Suisun Bay. APL had provided a burn-out Chief to assist, and he had worked with a Relief Engineer to start up the plant and get the lights on. APL followed this routine to ensure the assigned Chief would not be totally exhausted and unable to handle the job of getting the ship ready for sea.

In the past, the Chief would take the ship through the MARAD-mandated five-day trial to start up, perform a sea trial, and then go to sea. That was a 20-hour-per-day job lasting five days, after which the Chief still had to prepare the ship for sea. The burn-out Chief took the five days of all-day and all-night work so the assigned Chief could rest in the evenings and avoid being dangerously fatigued by the five-day event.

The plant was in good shape, and the burn-out Chief was an old-timer with one arm missing below the elbow. He had spent two years on the ship as Chief before it was laid up, and was a Port Engineer with APL. Lefty was well-known on the waterfront and had made a name for himself as an engineer with APL, both ashore and aboard ships. The man also ran a foundry, and was recognized as being multi-talented and highly competent.

During his two years as Chief aboard the *Hunter Victory* Lefty had built in some very desirable operating modifications. Freddie took a quick look around and made note of these upgrades, along with some things to share with the current Chief. They had to develop a list of items needed aboard, and Lefty had mentioned that he would help get as much aboard as had been removed during the layup when he was Chief.

Freddie committed to the ship and stayed aboard, with no intention of going back home. His days and nights for the next week were spent getting the ship ready, stowed, and crewed to shift the ship to Port Chicago, where it would be loaded with ammunition. This was a good moneymaker which guaranteed a 110% bonus (100% war zone pay plus an additional 10% bonus for hauling ammunition). He made up lists of tools, disposables, and other items needed to make the trip, as the ship had been stripped when it was laid up. Lefty, acting as the Port Engineer, got special tools aboard such as a welder, pipe threading machine, and other goodies that he knew the ship would need. Freddie followed Lefty around like a puppy dog, responding to his every need to allow him to help the ship. The two really synched up and enjoyed each other's company.

Their hard work ensured that the ship had a good supply of gear, plus an exceptional Blackgang crew from the MFOW to run its engineering side. Again, Lefty had put out the word that the ship would be a moneymaker to the MFOW union members who were looking for a well-running and good-paying job. Lefty had sailed with the MFOW for most of his Hawsepipe years, from when he first started going to sea as a Wiper up until he earned his Engineering license. The days were long and the nights were short, because Freddie knew that he had to develop the Blackgang into a well-running machine if they were to have a successful trip to and from Vietnam. Freddie had the good fortune to be able to shadow Lefty and learn of all the potential trouble areas aboard the *Hunter Victory*.

Loading ammunition at Port Chicago was another learning experience for Freddie. There were restrictions about all kinds of things: smoking areas were limited, hot work was forbidden, and so on. To offset these restrictions, Lefty had made arrangements to load some fuel in the bay and then top off in Subic Bay so they wouldn't have to handle that chore with a full load of ammunition (ammo).

Freddie had loaded fuel aboard a Victory, so he was well prepared to help the Chief, who had never bunkered a Victory ship. The amount of fuel would be adequate to get the ship from San Francisco to Subic Bay, with an additional 25% cushion for contingencies. The ship had some draft restrictions going up to Port Chicago, and the load of 500-pound bombs would put the ship down to her "marks" in the way of draft. Between the loading of stores and Blackgang supplies and taking on fuel, the ship was kept so busy that it was a week before she got away from Hunter's Point.

The next location, Port Chicago, was up-river from the Carquinez and Richmond-San Rafael Bridges. The transit from Hunter's Point was an all-day event. Freddie had organized a trial run of the engines the day before they left Hunter's Point to get everyone trained in the operation of the plant. The Captain was a new guy as Master, so the Chief clued him in regarding the procedure. The Captain was thankful, and made sure his Deck-side crew was aware and ready for the engine testing. The ship was to shift from Hunter's Point at 0800 hours the next day.

The pilot was aboard by 0700 hours. He was familiar with the pier where the ship was docked, and got the support tug to back up to the ship and run its engines to clear the mud which had collected against the hull. This would help with getting the ship away from the dock, since otherwise the built-up mud could hold it in place. The area had not been dredged for years, and some of the break-outs of other ships had been disastrous when trying to get away and out into the bay.

Freddie and the Chief had the ship's engines ready four hours ahead of time. They were confident, having run the plant and tested the engine ahead and astern, up to 5 rpm in both directions. Between the mud under the hull and extra lines to the dock, the ship had hardly moved at all during the engine testing.

Promptly at 0800 hours they got the first bell, "Standby," and the ship was pulled into the bay by the tug with a few bells and assists from the engine. The transit was slow, and it took time to get under the Bay Bridge, pass Treasure Island, and steam up the Sacramento River to Port Chicago. They docked at 1600 hours and were tied up and ready to sit down to a meal by 1700 hours. Lefty had been aboard for the whole time, just because he was curious to see how the ship would run after being laid up compared to when he had been her Chief. Freddie capitalized on that time to pick the older man's brain about the ship.

It took all of two weeks to load the ship with ammo. The last couple days were spent getting the crew aboard and dried out, as the old-timers had found a favorite bar in what was left of Port Chicago. During WWII a ship had exploded while being loaded there and leveled a good portion of the town. A bar and a few houses still remained, but the rest of the area adjacent to the ammunition bunkers built into the landscape had not been redeveloped.

The US Coast Guard was also aboard to oversee the loading of ammunition. They were very strict about all the restrictions and went everywhere on the ship, almost harassing the crew in their wake. Time seemed to drag, as the bombs had to be supported in place with lumber and cribbing to prevent them from moving around. The explosive components were separated from the bombs themselves to prevent any possible accidents. The extra time needed for all this, plus the actual mechanics of transporting the bombs and ammunition from the storage area to the ship, was tedious.

Freddie was on call with the Chief Electrician and Second Electrician to troubleshoot any winch problems, and did not get off the ship for the entire loading period. He had volunteered to stay aboard so that the Chief and other engineers could go home at night. Freddie was aboard to help out with any problems and back up the MEBA Relief Engineer who stood the watch from 1600 hours to 0800 hours each night. To better accommodate the fellow, Freddie found a place for him to sleep so that he didn't have to commute back and forth from the ship.

On a Tuesday morning at 0800 hours the ship had a tug tied up to help her get away from the dock with a full load of bombs and ammunition. Freddie made a late-night collection run to get the crew out of the bar and back aboard. They passed the ever-present US Coast Guard, who seemed to take exception to these characters who worked hard but also drank hard. Freddie felt like a mother hen. He also knew that these old-timers from the MFOW and MEBA were good seamen, and his Blackgang members were old pros who had sailed Victory ships for years. He supported them to get aboard and ensure that they had a full complement of crew.

Some of the Oilers and Firemen were a bit hungover, but attentive on the deck plates and doing their jobs. The Chief was in attendance and the plant had been made ready for sea for the last four hours by Freddie, the 4–8 Third Engineer, and the MEBA Relief Engineer. The Relief Engineer was signed off by 0630 and told to head home, so he packed his gear, cleaned up his bunk space, and walked off the ship to visit the MEBA hall for a good payoff.

The transit from Port Chicago to the Pilot Station outside the Golden Gate took all day, and the ship was escorted by a tug until she was past the Golden Gate and in open water. The ship stopped at the pilot station out past Mile Rock and dropped off the Pilot to the waiting Pilot Boat. The trip down the river had been uneventful and the plant had run well with the assistance of all the old-timer Oilers and Firemen, plus the Engineers who had signed on for the bonus pay. The *Hunter Victory's* history as a good feeder and a good overtime ship also contributed to its appeal.

After departing from San Francisco the ship headed into a squall, rolling lazily from port to starboard as she passed the Cliff House off to the port side. Freddie and the Chief breathed a sigh of relief to finally be at sea, and looked forward to the three weeks or more it would take to get to Vietnam. Their reported destination was to be the ammo port inland and up the river from the port of Saigon.

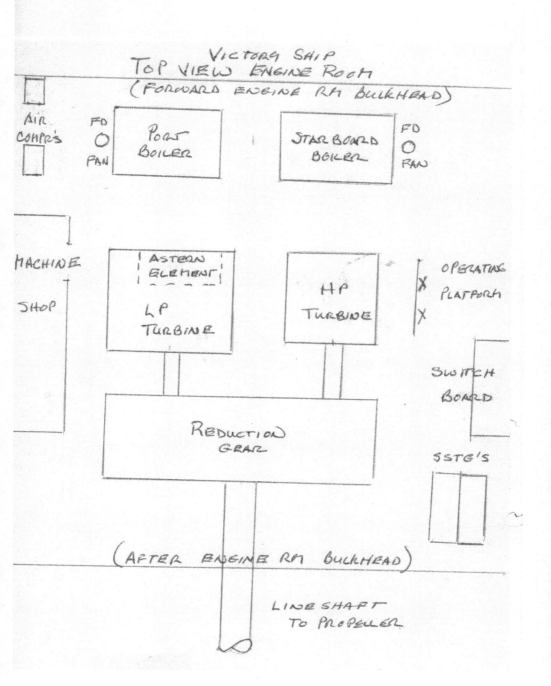

VICTORY SHIP
TOP VIEW ENGINE ROOM
(FORWARD ENGINE RM BULKHEAD)

AIR COMPR'S

FD O FAN

PORT BOILER

STARBOARD BOILER

FD O FAN

MACHINE SHOP

ASTERN ELEMENT

LP TURBINE

HP TURBINE

OPERATING PLATFORM
X
X

SWITCH BOARD

REDUCTION GEAR

SSTG'S

(AFTER ENGINE RM BULKHEAD)

LINE SHAFT TO PROPELLER

48

Victory Condenser - Air Ejector Systems

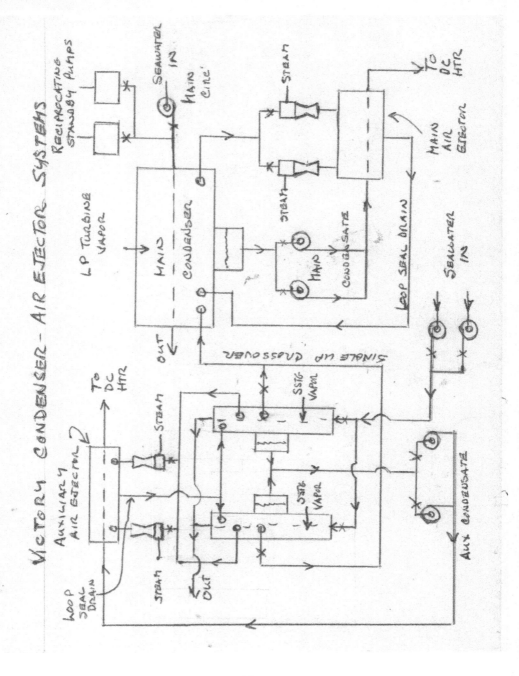

49

VICTORY SHIP DC ELECTRIC SYSTEM

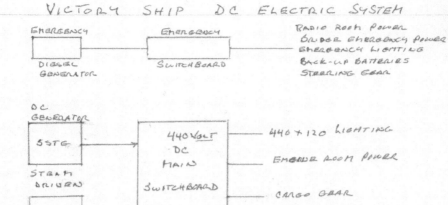

```
EMERGENCY              EMERGENCY              RADIO ROOM POWER
                                             BRIDGE EMERGENCY POWER
                                             EMERGENCY LIGHTING
DIESEL                 SWITCHBOARD           BACK-UP BATTERIES
GENERATOR                                    STEERING GEAR


DC
GENERATOR

  SSTG          →      440 VOLT       ──────  440 × 120 LIGHTING
                        DC
STEAM                  MAIN           ──────  ENGINE ROOM POWER
DRIVEN
                      SWITCHBOARD     ──────  CARGO GEAR

  SSTG          →                     ──────  STEERING GEAR

DC
GENERATOR
```

51

VICTORY SHIP EVAPORATOR

SEAWATER INLET

VENT

DEMISTER

DISTILLATE TO FRESH WATER TANKS

BAFFLES

VAPOR

INSPECTION MAINTENANCE DOOR

WATER LEVEL

SALTWATER INLET

CONDENSATE

BRINE

STEAM INLET

INSPECTION MAINTENANCE DOOR

The 6,000 horsepower *Hunter Victory* rode well with a full load of ammo, and about three or four hundred miles from San Francisco she emerged from the bad weather into clear blue seas and wide-open horizons. It was refreshing to be on deck or on the bridge and see the clear horizon surrounding the ship, with no smog or clouded skies.

At night during sunset hours, Freddie and the Chief would take their coffee to the bridge and witness the "green flash" just as the sun went down. The phenomenon is a just-for-a-moment event as the sun passes the horizon. It results from looking at the sun through a greater and greater thickness of atmosphere as you look lower and lower in the sky. Water vapor in the atmosphere absorbs the yellow and orange colors in white sunlight, and air molecules scatter the violet light; in other words, it results from the refraction of sunlight. The phenomenon is rarely seen ashore due to the haze and smog which lies on the horizon and filters out the quick moment of emerald green flash.

Freddie began making a full round of the engine room and other parts of the ship on a regular daily basis. He made up a work list and posted it in the machine shop to allow those engineers who wanted to work overtime to pick the jobs they were most comfortable with. Some needed to have Freddie direct them as to what to do, and others didn't want overtime and were happy just standing their watch.

Looking over the Unlicensed, he saw that some were talented and wanted the overtime. One Oiler was a good welder, so he was assigned to perform various repairs in the engine room and on deck as needed. The Electricians were busy in both the engine room and on deck doing clean up in preparation for cargo operations in Vietnam, and also working on motor controllers which needed cleaning and adjustment. The Wipers were busy cleaning up the engine room and also proposed a complete bilge cleanup and paint job. Extra paint had been ordered for this job, which had been started but not completed during Lefty's time aboard the ship.

Lefty had taken the effort to upgrade certain systems to make operating the ship easier. These included the following:

- Valve bypasses installed around the boiler economizers

These allowed the ship to keep underway in the event that a leak developed in the 20-year-old economizers. Otherwise a boiler would have to be shut down while tubes were plugged or other steps taken to repair the failure. This upgrade allowed the Economizer to be bypassed so that repairs could be done later.

- DC heater pressure supply regulator relocation

The controls which maintained constant pressure in the DC heater to heat and scrub the boiler feed free of entrained oxygen were originally mounted at the top of the engine room. These had been moved to the operating platform by the main engine throttles, removing the need to climb all the way to the top of the fidley to make adjustments.

- Re-piping of the saltwater cooling pipes on various systems

The saltwater piping had been changed from the original mild steel to brass piping. This prevented the wastage which was common on many of the systems, like the refrigeration heat exchangers (condensers).

- Boiler water level controls

These controls were very basic single-element devices which simply reacted to the level in the steam drum when operating the feedwater control valves on each boiler.

When the ship was in bad weather the controls had a tendency to feed too much into the boiler, so shims were inserted in the appropriate locations to offset the false signals. Lefty had also overhauled the complete controls arrangement to make them more responsive.

- Feed pump overhaul including packing and controls

Port operation used reciprocating feed pumps which were conducive to the slow steaming conditions but had a tendency to move erratically. Lefty had overhauled the coordinated controls of the steam-drum-mounted controls as well as those which fed the steam to the pumps so that they all worked smoothly.

Sea operation required the use of a turbine-driven feed pump which was prone to erratic behavior while trying to maintain a fixed and constant feed pressure, plus the pump packing had a tendency to leak. These controls had been overhauled and a new style of Teflon-type packing was installed which did not wear out like the packing materials normally used in the past.

- Reciprocating fuel pump leak-off collection

The normal arrangement in the boiler room allowed expected leakage from the pump end of the reciprocating fuel pumps to leak down across the pumps into a collection area at the deck level. This was a messy fire hazard. A cement collection area added to the top of the pump enabled the Firemen to collect and dump any fuel which leaked out before it reached the deck. This allowed the whole area to remain tidy, and even be cleaned and painted.

Coordinating the work of the Blackgang kept Freddie busy, and he found it harder to stay ahead of his paperwork. Looking for someone to handle that chore, he discovered that a Third Engineer and one of the Oilers were part-time tax preparers when they were ashore, and asked if they would be interested in earning some overtime. Freddie would approve all the overtime work, after which they would be responsible for handling the collection and filling out the necessary company forms. This allowed Freddie to devote more time to organizing work, and even doing some of the work himself.

He noted that the Second Engineer was a quiet guy who also had a First Engineer's license. The man seemed happy to work overtime as needed to keep the boiler controls and soot blowers and such in good shape, including doing the twice-daily boiler chemistry tests and treatment. Freddie kept the Chief apprised of all these changes, and got his approval before putting them into effect.

This Chief had been schooled by an old-time Chief Engineer who maintained that the only time the Chief was needed in the engine room was in the event of a blackout or if someone needed to be fired. This left Freddie with the responsibility of running the Blackgang by himself. The Chief was busy most days approving the overtime Freddie submitted each week and entering all the preventative maintenance and repairs from his reports into the history 3-by-5 cards in his office. The Chief also had to keep in touch with the Captain, and they had cocktail hour each day before dinner and played cards well into the morning at times if conditions allowed.

Within the usual three weeks, they took arrival in Subic Bay and were told that they would be anchored well off the pier due to the fact they were carrying ammo. The fuel barge was to be alongside within an hour of when they would be dropping the anchors. Freddie had been assigned to take on bunkers with the Second Engineer, as the Chief felt that he was better prepared to do that. The Second seemed to have a good handle on the process and the whole bunkering effort took about five hours. Freddie told the Chief that he needed to go ashore to get some gifts for his girlfriend and that he would be back on the evening launch. The Second would be aboard in the meantime to handle any unforeseen emergencies.

Freddie took a quick shower, dressed, and took some money to buy things that he had in mind to take home to Cindy. He also wanted to visit Rocky's bar to see some of the friends he had made during his first visit to Subic Bay. His intentions were to be back aboard the ship by no later than 2200 hours (10:00pm). Little did he know that this would be the start of an odyssey that would span some ten days.

He stopped at Rocky's, had a couple of beers, and bought food and drinks for all the bar girls who had been part of the group from years ago. Then Freddie headed to the stores to buy his gifts. The items he was interested in and thought Cindy would like filled up a hand-carry bag which he could manage on and off the launch and while climbing up the gangway. Souvenirs in hand, he made the launch and settled down for the long run out to the *Hunter Victory,* as they were the furthest ship in the anchorage out from the pier. When they finally reached the spot, you can imagine his surprise at discovering that the ship was nowhere to be seen!

Freddie made the launch look around, but sure enough the ship was gone, so he had to head back to Olongapo to wait until the local MSTS office opened in the morning. Upon returning to shore, he walked out through the gate to the first restaurant-bar and found four of his fellow crew members sitting there. Their stories were the same as his: Each had planned on being aboard before the ship sailed, only to ride the launch out to where the *Hunter Victory* had been anchored and find it had already departed. They commiserated over food and beer before settling in to wait out the night.

In the morning they headed to the MSTS office to determine what had happened. Freddie ended up being the senior officer present, so he asked the questions to the first person they found in the office. The answer, quick and curt and delivered with a kind of disdain, was that "The ship had emergency orders to sail." Left unsaid was the fact that the MSTS fellow felt the five were a bunch of characters who had missed the ship.

The group included a Wiper, a Second Cook and Baker, and two Deck Hands – Ordinary Seamen. Freddie hadn't known any of their names except for the Wiper, who was a good guy and an old-timer in the MFOW. They were given tickets for a bus to Manila and the address of the APL office there.

The bus ride was long, hot, and dusty, with no air conditioning and numerous stops at what felt like every small village between Olongapo and Manila. They arrived just after noon and had to wait for the APL person in charge to get back from drinking his lunch. He was an old-time Captain who had picked a plum job as APL office head in Manila, and he was not happy to be responsible for five stranded crew members. Freddie kept his tongue as the Captain berated him and his shipmates. In amongst the rest of the tirade, he told them that they would each get a $50 draw, a passport, a place to stay, and a plane ticket to Saigon.

Unlike the rest of the guys, Freddie was not interested in drinking and chasing women, and just wanted a quick meal and an air conditioned room with a clean bed. This was a new experience for him, and he didn't know if he would lose time and money for having missed the ship. In the morning their passports were issued, plane tickets supplied, and they all climbed on the bus to the airport. Unbeknown to Freddie and his shipmates, this would be just the beginning of their adventure.

Their plane was an Air France flight which departed on time and headed towards Saigon. The flight was a mess, as all of Freddie's shipmates were drunk or hungover, leaving him to make out their paperwork. Then the plane's arrival in Saigon was disrupted by the fact that the Vietcong (VC) began shelling the Tan Son Nhat airport as they were coming in for their landing. The plane powered off back into the sky and headed towards Cambodia's Phnom Penh airport to take on enough fuel to make it to the airport in Bangkok, Thailand.

Freddie's shipmates were elated, as they had already enjoyed an APL-subsidized night to party in Manila and now would get to party in Bangkok. He, on the other hand, was miserable, and only wanted to get back to the ship so he could add time on his license and earn money! An APL representative met the group at the airport in Bangkok and they got another $50 draw, a place to stay, and plane tickets to Saigon in two days. His shipmates pulled out all the stops and were out enjoying the night life of Bangkok while Freddie shopped for a toothbrush, clothes, and underwear.

The two days passed slowly, and then they were in another APL bus on the way to the airport, with another $50 draw to tide them over in Saigon. APL supplied a bus and booked the group into the Hotel Continental which was opposite the Floating Restaurant that had been bombed early in the Vietnam War. Freddie's shipmates were beside themselves, as they had tasted the women in the Philippines and Thailand, and now they were out after Vietnamese. Meanwhile Freddie found a place for a good meal and a cold beer, and questioned the APL representative about where the ship was and how they would get there.

The *Hunter Victory* was anchored upriver from Saigon where all the ammo ships were unloaded, and to get there they had to take military transportation and then a launch. That final leg of the journey was anti-climactic, with four hungover shipmates and a rough ride on a truck followed by a long river ride to the ship. The *Hunter Victory* had never looked better, and Freddie was happy to make it up the gangway and see the faces of the Chief Engineer and Captain. The two had many questions, and also offered some apologies about leaving them in Olongapo. The good news was that Freddie would not lose any pay. As dictated by the union's agreement with APL, he would be paid for any normal overtime or bonus that he would have received if he was aboard.

They had already been at anchor for two days, and the discharge of the ammo had only started the day Freddie arrived back on the ship. The offloading of the ammo was long and tedious, and the US Coast Guard was aboard to monitor the process as well. They would be at anchor for two weeks or more, and then they would be going to Sattahip, Thailand. The same restrictions that they had been working under at Port Chicago were again in full force at the ammo anchorage.

The offloading was further delayed as the military could not handle the amount of ammo that was aboard and scheduled to be delivered to Saigon. The delay lasted two weeks, so they did not set sail for Thailand as soon as they had expected to. The ship was actually being used as a warehouse, and ammo was being removed on an as-needed basis. At night, when the crew was sitting on deck, they could see some of the bombs they had carried being dropped within visual distance of the ship. The Coast Guard guys told them that the military had sensors to detect movement within five miles of the ship. If those sensors were triggered, the bombs would fall to take out whatever was moving around—which, in most cases, was a cow or some other animal.

Being anchored up-river of Saigon for more than two weeks did have some benefits, including the fact that Freddie was not spending any money ashore and also had a sober crew he could put to work catching up on maintenance and repairs. This gave them an excellent opportunity to complete many of the repair items which could not be done at sea, as they required equipment to be shut down. Freddie caught up on studying for his license, and even had time to read some paperbacks, such as Louis L'Amour's Westerns.

The normal delays associated with offloading cargo to the military in Vietnam were legendary, so no one seemed to be too upset. They would be in the war zone for about a month, plus they would receive the additional 10% ammunition bonus. The crew was working on the jobs which Freddie had set up, and the Second Engineer had filled in while Freddie was flying around Asia trying to catch the ship. The Chief had picked up the slack and was very happy to have Freddie back to handle the workload. Everyone was ready to get back to sea and feel a cool breeze, as the river was hot and humid, and everyone was itching to get off the ship and have a meal ashore. There was no shore launch at the anchorage, though, as the area was totally secure on account of the dangerous cargo aboard.

Freddie organized a work group to water wash the boilers while the ship was anchored in the river. He had picked up some tips from the Chief Engineer on the *Azalea City*, and now utilized that approach on the *Hunter Victory*. Once the boiler was cooled down, the furnace was opened to allow access to the economizer and the area beneath so that they could wash the tubes and inspect same afterwards. They used the water in the boiler itself, as it had chemicals which could neutralize the acidic effects of the sulfur-laden soot on the internal boiler tube exterior.

Pressurizing the boiler with air and hooking up a hose to the blowdown line allowed the boiler to be blown down, and also allowed use of the blow down to wash the boiler internals. The Wipers assisted the Second and pumped the remnants from the furnace overboard. The whole process of cleaning, drying out, and steaming up both boilers took the better part of a week. Before they closed up the boilers they completed any necessary refractory repairs and took a close look at all the visible tubes.

The engine room was getting cleaned up, the work of the Wipers was very noticeable from top to bottom, and most of the steel work had been completed. The Blackgang was getting tired of working overtime, so Freddie told everyone to plan on taking some time off when they docked in Sattahip. The ship would be at a dock and there was a group of restaurants and bars not too far from the facility where they would be unloading the last of the ammo.

The most memorable events of the stay in Sattahip were the dinners which the group from the ship attended on most evenings. Ten people could be fed for $20 USD with rice, fish, chicken, and vegetables, plus a liter of cold beer for each as well as a fruit plate to finish off the meal. It was a chance to relax, and everyone got to take a turn at treating the rest of their shipmates.

Freddie had reached an agreement with the Chief to give time off to all the watchstanders by having them stand twelve-hour watches followed by twenty-four hours off. This was possible since the ship's stay was expected to last at least two weeks. The long breaks were also important since the unbearable temperature and humidity caused everyone to tire easily.

The ammo they delivered to this port would supply the B-52 aircraft that flew in and out of Thailand on their bombing runs into Vietnam. The day workers put in eight-hour workdays and took the weekends off to allow everyone a chance to relax and rest up. Soon they would be heading back to the States on the long trip across the Pacific aboard an empty ship.

On the way back home, Freddie realized that he was going to be close to having enough time to sit for his Chief Engineer's license. With the time on the *Los Angeles* plus this first trip on the *Hunter Victory* he might have as much as ten months of sea time. He dearly wanted to get off and spend time with Cindy, but realized that he had a golden opportunity to get all the time he needed by staying on the *Hunter Victory* for another trip. Of course, there was no guarantee that the ship would still be needed and remain in operation once she arrived in San Francisco. The ship had a good reputation, though, and the Port Engineer, Lefty, had apprised APL that the ship and the crew were the best of the Victory ships that APL was husbanding.

During the three-week voyage the crew made a concentrated effort to clean up the ship, both on deck and in the engine room, as a show for the APL folks and the MARAD personnel who would be visiting the ship once she was docked in San Francisco. A week outside of San Francisco they were informed that they would be taking Christmas mail to the troops in Vietnam, and they were dubbed the "Santa Claus Special." This became a big pitch for APL regarding how well they operated their government ships, so the Chief put in for a number of enhancements to upgrade the engine room and the Captain asked for some upgrades on the bridge as well.

When the *Hunter Victory* arrived in California, Lefty visited the ship along with Harry Morgan, the APL Senior Port Engineer. They had a powwow with the Captain, Chief Engineer, Chief Mate, and First Engineer in the Captain's office to lay out the political issues of the upcoming trip to carry Christmas presents and mail to the US troops in Vietnam. They would have two weeks to do repairs and load cargo, after which they would be expected to sail to Vietnam and arrive in plenty of time to deliver their precious cargo to the troops. Freddie was extremely busy, but managed to get off each night since the ship was docked on the San Francisco waterfront at a new repair outfit's pier used by a company called Service Engineering.

Cindy was thrilled to see him, and realized that they had to take advantage of the short time they had to catch up, share meals, and enjoy some quality time. The workdays started early and the nights were sometimes long, so Freddie did not get home until 2000 hours (8:00pm). No matter what time he showed up, Cindy never complained, and always seemed to be able to make whatever time they shared pleasant and memorable. Freddie let her know that he would be off for at least two months after this trip so that he could test for his Chief Engineer's license.

The boilers were shut down for the requested repairs and upgrades, such as the fitting of new stainless-steel inspection doors on the superheater and some repairs to the handhole plates on the sectional headers. The start-up of the plant was assisted by the Service Engineering group, which supplied all the necessary equipment, stores, and such to get the ship on its way. Between long days on the ship and romancing in the evening, Freddie was not getting much sleep. He was young, though, and he was being supported by his now-mentor Lefty, who attended the ship each day to make sure that Service Engineering was doing their work correctly.

There were photo-ops for the unions and the news media, since APL was using the opportunity to show off their expertise in handling ships and supporting the troops in Vietnam. Finally the plant was up, the cargo was aboard, all the stores and supplies were stowed, and the day came to leave and head back to Vietnam. Between the six weeks at sea sailing out and back to the States, plus the port time at Saigon and Da Nang in Vietnam, the trip would take at least three months. This would put the ship back in San Francisco around January, meaning that Christmas would most likely be spent at sea. Freddie was getting anxious to get his Chief Engineer's license and spend more quality time with his lady friend.

The trip was a thing to write home about, particularly after Freddie's recent adventures. There were no breakdowns and no problems with the crew. The ship didn't even leave anyone on the beach due to sudden emergency sailing orders. The *Hunter Victory* received VIP treatment in every port, enabling them to unload her cargo very quickly and efficiently. Their entries and departures from the ports of Saigon and Da Nang were accomplished swiftly, with quick clearances, senior pilots, and new tugboats to assist with docking and undocking.

In exactly three months, the *Hunter Victory* docked in San Francisco and was informed that she would be laying up once again. Lefty was aboard, as he was still working as a Port Engineer in between quick relief trips as Chief Engineer on ships which needed help. After the crew had been paid off, Freddie was hired as an outside contractor to work with Lefty and Service Engineering. Together they completed the items required by MARAD to lay up the ship and send it to the Reserve Fleet at Suisun Bay. Throughout the process, Freddie was looking forward to getting his Chief Engineer's license!

The time aboard the *Hunter Victory* was memorable, as Freddie applied the tactics that he had acquired from his mentor, Lefty, and also from his shipmate, the young Chief of the *Hunter Victory*. What he had learned during his time aboard as First was to capitalize on the varied talents of the Blackgang and look past the oddities of each in order to concentrate on what could be used to better the operation of the ship. This experience would be utilized for the rest of Freddie's career as a marine engineer and in associated work.

Have you ever reached the pinnacle of your expectations? Can you imagine the rush pilots feel the first time they're able to fly that jet plane after all their schooling, classes, and simulator tests? Now Freddie was about to reach a long-sought milestone of his career: earning his Chief Engineer's license. He had the required one year of sea time on his First Engineer's license, which he verified at the USCG licensing office in San Francisco. Now he had to study at Law's School of Marine Engineering and prepare for the test.

Freddie used the old VW Bug for his commute between San Francisco and Oakland. He would drive Cindy to work, then head to Oakland for class, and leave in time to pick her up when she was done for the day. They'd have a quick meal, after which he would spend the evening studying. Law's was true to its founder's promise that he could almost guarantee that you would pass if you paid attention to the information which he shared and expected you to absorb. This had worked for Freddie each time he had raised his license, first from Third Assistant to Second Assistant and then from Second Assistant to First Assistant.

After three weeks Freddie felt he was ready, and he knew that if he did not pass a section he could always retake an exam. He made an appointment to start on a Monday morning and surprised himself by breezing through the examination, finishing up on Wednesday at about 1400 hours (2:00pm). He went across the street to the Golden Bull to get a cold beer and a burger while anxiously waiting the hour and a half they had told him it would take to grade the test. Precisely at 1530 hours (3:30pm) he was back at the desk, and noticed a smile on the face of the secretary who had been there for all his tests. She said one word: "Congratulations."

Freddie met with the US Coast Guard Commander who was in charge of the Testing Facility to get his license. The Commander offered him his congratulations and noted that the US Coast Guard would be interested in hiring someone like him if he was interested. Freddie courteously replied that he was not 100% sure where he was going now, but in the back of his head, he dreamt of taking a new ship out of the shipyard as Chief Engineer.

The only person that Freddie really wanted to share this with was his girlfriend, Cindy. He gathered up his study materials and new license and headed home, stopping to buy a bottle of champagne and some glasses along the way. He arrived home in time to shower and clean up before picking Cindy up from work. That night they celebrated and talked about the journey they had shared and each other's plans for the future.

Though Cindy never pressured him to quit working as a sailor, Freddie developed the idea that she would prefer if he stopped going to sea, and wanted him home on a full-time basis. She was 100% supportive of anything that he wanted to do, and he in turn wanted to provide her with that same kind of opportunity. Truth be told, spending ten months a year for the last five years sailing on all kinds of ships had left him kind of fatigued with the whole process.

The goal of getting his Chief Engineer's license had now been attained, and the other distant dream was to take a new ship out of the shipyard as Chief Engineer. That was a far reach, though, as he did not have a permanent job with any company and there weren't that many ships being built. The industry was somewhat stagnant when it came to new technology.

He felt the need to try something different. Freddie also knew that he had to learn how to troubleshoot electrical problems and read an electrical schematic. He understood the theory he had learned at CMA, but the practical aspects involved in being a troubleshooting technician were still beyond his capabilities.

For a number of months Freddie took MEBA night-relief jobs, which were lucrative and brought in money so he could stay home and enjoy the domestic scene. He realized that he enjoyed this lifestyle with Cindy and looked forward to spending time with her. He was not anxious to get back on a ship. So Freddie started looking at the help-wanted part of the newspaper and networking to see what jobs he might be able to get with his new Chief Engineer's license.

In looking at various jobs which he thought he could qualify for, Freddie had a rude awakening. He'd expected that having a Chief Engineer's license would make him a shoo-in for any job ashore. It was a surprise to discover his hard-won license didn't carry the same significance on land which it did at sea.

His first attempt was an interview with Southern Pacific Railroad as a Repair Engineer. That application was vetoed when he presented his credentials as a CMA graduate to the interviewers, who had all attended Stanford and the University of California. Freddie didn't pass the physical, but was fairly certain that was just a convenient excuse to cover up the fact they felt his qualifications were inadequate.

The next job he applied for was an Engineer's job with a diesel repair shop. That did not go well as Freddie's skill at reading electrical prints was lacking, and the interviewer told him that he did not have time to teach him. This wasn't a surprise, as Freddie had already known he needed more experience on the subject, having never been challenged to master it before.

The next job he interviewed for was with a company which made industrial burners and controls. Coen Company was a family-owned business located in Burlingame, California, and the interviewer was an old Chief Engineer who understood the depth of experience possessed by marine engineers and how they fit the need for Coen's Service Engineers. After their lunch interview, the old Chief (who was the Service Manager) asked Freddie when he wanted to start work. He asked for a couple of days to think about it so he could be sure that he could commit to the full-time work and reduced pay in comparison to going to sea.

The obstacle, if there was one, centered around Cindy and whether she would be willing to part with her lifestyle in San Francisco and leave with him to go to God-knows-where. Stopping at a bar, Freddie had a cold beer, took out a sheet of paper, and wrote down all the good points of taking the job on one side and all the not-so-good points on the other. He knew that Cindy did not really know what she wanted to do, but—more importantly—she did not have the finances to go to college or take on a new job which provided some advancement. He felt obligated to provide that opportunity out of gratitude for the stability she had brought into his life.

The conversation that he had with Cindy that night was an open forum, and she was perceptive enough to realize that Freddie had a commitment to her and a deep affection for her. She noted that she wanted to go to college, and leaving San Francisco might prevent her from doing that. Freddie replied that she could go to college anywhere that they might move to. To this she responded that she could not afford to go to college and share in their expenses. He said that he could always work and provide for them in some manner, plus he had saved some of the money he had earned while sailing.

The ultimate solution, he proclaimed, would be to get married. Cindy was dumbfounded, and told him that he did not have to do that as their present arrangement was adequate for her. She said that she would go along with the idea of moving so that Freddie could work for Coen Company, but that she needed time to think about this marriage thing.

The final decision came a couple of days later, when Cindy suggested that they go to Lehr's Steak House where they first connected. Over dinner, they shared the frightening reality that each of them had witnessed broken marriages in their families, and they were both concerned about that possibility. The other issue which concerned the two of them was children. Again, due to the broken marriages they had witnessed, they had both seen children suffer in the wake of divorces and broken homes. They agreed on another fact, though: that they were in love, and wanted to spend time together for as long as possible. Cindy affirmed that she wanted Freddie to pursue whatever his dreams were and that she put no restrictions on that part of their relationship. What was not said, but understood, was the fact that she would appreciate the same support on his part in the relationship.

Within the week, the offer from Coen Company was accepted and they applied for a marriage license. They were immediately married by a justice of the peace, with a formal marriage to follow at a later date. And they embarked, as husband and wife, on what was to be an international tour exposing them to many cultures and locations.

Coen needed someone to be a Service Engineer in the Midwest, so Freddie and Cindy picked Ann Arbor, Michigan. A classmate of Freddie's was studying for his MBA at the University of Michigan and claimed that, of all the places in the Midwest, Ann Arbor was the best. First, though, Freddie had to complete at least six months of training and indoctrination as required by the Coen Company Service Department. He thus started his life as a nine-to-five worker commuting between San Francisco and the Coen Company offices in Burlingame, about fifteen miles down the peninsula.

In that six-month period Freddie learned the basics of the Coen Company structure and products, and the focus that he was to assume as a Service Engineer. The thought of working with boilers and steam plants or boiler-supported operations was not a challenge for him. The parts which remained mysterious were the electrical prints, and troubleshooting the relay-based controls produced in the factory in Burlingame.

Guys years younger than Freddie spent days teaching him about the Coen Fyr-Compak units which could be welded to the front of a boiler, with all the controls and piping necessary to operate that boiler unattended. This concept was well accepted in the shoreside industries, and also aboard some of the older Keystone T2 tankers in the US-flagged fleet which had automated their firerooms.

Once the six-month indoctrination was completed Freddie felt more comfortable, but realized that he lacked hands-on experience with troubleshooting electrical problems and reading the electrical prints which Coen used. Freddie came to the stark realization that he was not a fast learner. Despite being a slow learner, though, he was willing to work hard to master the technical aspects of any work and could, with time, be as good or better than his peers who seemed to grasp the new challenges easily.

Coen arranged for their belongings to be shipped to Ann Arbor, Michigan, though at the time the moving van was being packed they didn't yet have an address to direct it towards. Freddie and Cindy loaded a few things into their VW Bug and headed east. The trip across the country was an adventure, but Freddie was more concerned with beating the moving van to Ann Arbor and finding a place for them to stay than he was with a sightseeing trip through the heartland of the US. Taking the Lincoln Highway, they blitzed the run in three and a half days. In between hailstorms and long stretches of straight highway lined by corn fields, they spent the nights in some motels and any place they could find along the way.

The classmate who was attending the University of Michigan tipped them off as to where to stay and where to look for a place to live. The college town was truly Midwestern, and its small-town character was tinged with the liberal-type college environment common to all major university locales. Cindy took up the chore of finding a place in the want-ads and discovered a small house on Pear Street in Ann Arbor. They went to check it out on the same day they arrived, and loved the quaint place with its detached garage within sight of the University of Michigan campus and its associated hospital.

The residence was found, and the moving van arrived to unload within a day or so. They stocked up on essentials to make their new home, and since Freddie had no obligations with Coen Company for that week he helped Cindy set up house and learn the community. They adored the little house and settled down immediately, starting off their marriage with the adventure of traveling across America, meeting new friends and neighbors, and diving into a profession outside the maritime industry.

Freddie was indoctrinated into the Service Engineer business by some old-timers who lived in the surrounding states. He flew into Ohio and Illinois and stayed in motels while visiting the plants where Coen equipment was installed and would need start-up and service calls. The majority of the Service Engineers were former Navy guys, and some were CMA graduates who had learned of the work from classmates or by networking via the grapevine.

Within a few weeks Freddie was cleared to handle things by himself, and was told to head to Chicago to help with the post-commission modifications of a duct burner. This was new to Freddie, and the job would be the turning point in his career involving the black art of reading an electrical print and troubleshooting actual controls in the field.

Chicago's main sewage plant was on the outskirts of a village named Stickney. It was the largest sewage plant in the United States, and its five processing lines could each treat fifty tons of sewage per hour. It was an older design, but still the textbook example of how to treat a large volume of waste. The Coen installation was a duct burner with an in-line gas-fired arrangement in the exhaust stack of the process for the sewage treatment plant. The process worked as follows:

- Sewage was pumped into the plant and treated with ferric chloride.
- The chemically treated sewage was fed onto huge rotating drums with heavy cloth under a negative pressure, which drew the liquid out of the sewage sludge.

- The semi-dried sludge was ejected from the drum into a duct, where it mixed with the heat from the boilers' exhaust.
- The dried sludge was collected and barged to farmers downriver from Stickney.
- The effluent was exhausted into the atmosphere.

That exhaust duct was where the Coen duct burner was installed. The problem was that, in an attempt to clean up the stacks from the sewage treatment plant, an exhaust-water-scrubber had been installed. This cooled and kind-of-cleaned the exhaust, but created another problem: a nasty haze which blew into the surrounding developments across a freeway adjacent to the sewage plant. This haze was tolerated for years until the local government was forced to fix the problem.

The answer was to burn the effluent using a Coen duct burner. A duct burner was designed to fit the inside dimensions of the exhaust duct, with vertical six-inch diameter gas pipes every eighteen inches or so featuring winged burners one on top of another. The moisture-laden exhaust passed through the duct burner structure, which burned away the nasty haze, resulting in clear stacks for the first time in years.

The Service Engineer who had started the burner ran into problems, so he just used a jumper wire to bypass the controls. This allowed the duct burner to start up and perform for the ceremony to show the public and officials how the system would work in the future. The cleanup and final installation were to be Freddie's responsibility for the next year. During that time he would eventually have the good fortune to meet another Service Engineer from a controls outfit who helped him learn to read and troubleshoot electrical circuitry, after which Freddie would become very proficient with controls and their design.

For the next two years Freddie was working all over the Midwest, sometimes spending more time away from home than he had back when he was going to sea. Cindy, in the meantime, had enrolled in the local community college and found her niche as a Respiratory Therapist. The local University Hospital and adjacent St. Joseph's Hospital were leaders in that field and part of the sophisticated team which offered some of the best medical care in the Midwest. This kept her extremely busy, and occupied her time during those occasions when Freddie had to spend weeks away working in different parts of the four or five states closest to Ann Arbor.

Freddie worked hard, and even when he found himself thrown into some bizarrely-designed installations he was usually able to manage to start them up. If he had a problem, he could always call on the design engineers or his boss, Bob. He knew he had passed a milestone the day he called Bob for help with a particularly bad design and his boss told him he had no ideas to offer, and that Freddie would just have to work it out on his own. That was the turning point in his career with Coen. He had reached the point where he was capable of handling sophisticated design installation problems by himself.

In the 1970s, Coen Company burners and controls were considered to be the most sophisticated in the United States, and they were also installed in some locations in Europe and Asia. Freddie was responsible for the area bounded by Wisconsin on the west, New York on the east, and Ohio, Kentucky, and Illinois to the south. He bought a Chevrolet Vega station wagon and drove the wheels off that car in summer, winter, spring, and fall. It was his first experience driving in the snow and changing tires from standard tread to studded snow tires for the winter.

He was kind of like a seaman working ashore, living out of his suitcase and driving hundreds of miles a day to and from work locations. Just as he had met different races and ethnic groups of people when he went to sea, Freddie now found himself meeting countryside folks in the South whose lifestyle was completely foreign to him. These included hard-working men and women who drank hard and worked hard, as well as unique individuals who designed some very sophisticated plants and processes. Some plants dating all the way back to the 1800s were still in operation and vital to the industrial Midwest. Detroit was the car manufacturing center of the United States, and Toledo, Ohio and other areas close by had steel manufacturing plants. Freddie was amazed to discover how diverse the country was in the makeup of its people, and how industrious the general population was all over the Midwest.

The Midwest, with its four seasons, was also completely foreign to Freddie and Cindy, who had both been raised in California and were used to that state's year-long mild climate. Their first exposure to dramatic weather changes occurred during the frantic activity in July when they arrived in Ann Arbor, Michigan. Everyone was busy going to the lakes, barbequing, and doing everything out-of-doors. All of the sudden in September, when the weather changed, everyone disappeared into their homes, never to be seen again until the spring. Clothes had to be changed between seasons, and summer clothes were put away when the snow started to fall. They learned how to prepare a vehicle to travel during the winter, a process which could add an extra hour to each workday:

- Wake up, get dressed, and put on the coffee.
- Put on cold weather clothes to go out and start up the car, turning the heater and defroster up to full blast.
- Head back inside the house (taking off all the coats and hats) and eat breakfast.
- Pack a thermos of coffee and dress up in coat, hat, and gloves, then scrape the ice off the windshield and get into the nice warm car.
- Drive the hour (or however long) to the job site and work in the snow until it was time to drive home.
- Repeat the process until the weekend.

The change of seasons eventually brought people back outdoors, and they returned to their frantic efforts to enjoy the good weather of the spring, summer, and fall until it was snow season once again. Freddie and Cindy were lucky to meet some very nice folks and actually enjoyed the two-plus years they had in Ann Arbor and the Midwest.

Freddie worked in many of the states around Michigan, and drove to the east, south, and west for weeks at a time. Coen Company installations were very popular throughout the Midwest, and for the next two years Freddie's time was filled with some very interesting work. Notable jobs included:

- Bay City, Michigan power plant conversion from coal-firing to crude-oil-firing boilers using Coen equipment. This included taking air quality samples to prove the effluent was within national standards guidelines. For the better part of a year, Freddie commuted between Ann Arbor and Bay City daily instead of staying in a motel. It was a huge job by Coen standards, and he was challenged daily to keep ahead of the job progress and completion milestones.
- Duct burner installations in various locations, such as the Stickney sewage plant and a Detroit Diesel engine test facility outside Detroit. Finalization of the Stickney sewage plant installation took months, and required a week-long stay in Chicago. The Detroit Diesel plant installation was unique, since it was an oil-fired duct burner (unlike the Stickney duct burner, which was gas-fired). Both of these locations were one-off type designs. This led to trouble with design faults which Freddie resolved with simple engineering procedures and diagnosis.
- One installation of a gas-fired duct burner was in a coal-fired plant in the St. Louis area that was based upon what is now called a SNOX process which removes sulfur dioxide, nitrogen oxides, and particulates from the flue gases. The sulfur is recovered as concentrated sulfuric acid and the nitrogen oxides are reduced to free nitrogen. The Coen duct burner added heat to the process to change the SO_2 to SO_3 via a catalyst to produce the sulfuric acid. The installation was a prototype designed by a US chemical company.
- Rendering plant where they processed dead animals to make tallow or grease and animal protein meal. Nasty smell all day long while trying to manage the setting of the Coen equipment. The smell was a challenge, but no more so than the days spent at the sewage plant in Stickney.
- Learning to use a fire's shape and color to diagnose problems when setting the Coen burners and controls. Freddie's expertise reached the point that he could set the fuel-air ratio to almost acceptable standards by appearance alone before using an Orsat flue gas testing apparatus to final set the burner. This was a point of pride among Service Engineers, who loved to demonstrate their talents by creating a square-shaped flame which stopped just short of the back wall of the boiler and was within the EPA air quality limits of the time.
- Shipboard Coen burner installations and controls on the old ships which carried ore and steel between the ports in Michigan and Ohio on the Great Lakes. Freddie experienced a sense of *déjà vu* walking into an engine room and seeing the Coen boiler automation on boilers such as he had worked with on Victory ships and C2 type vessels. On the Great Lakes some of these old ships had been around since the 1930s or before, with crews that started out as cabin boys and were now engineers.

Freddie's biggest challenge was learning to troubleshoot the Coen electrical drawings which applied to the jobs he was working on. In Stickney, he had a lot of trouble trying to sort out what mistakes had been made when the contractor electrician wired up the control panel. Freddie was losing his mind, as he was not good at that sort of thing and did not know how to troubleshoot using a volt-ohm meter. Fortunately, a Hagan Controls technician walked by and asked what was going on.

Within a short period of time this very patient and friendly guy changed Freddie's world, and it was as if a light bulb turned on inside his head. Mind you, during the early 1970s the controls were all relay-based in their design and construction, as electronic components did not show up until the late 1970s. Freddie was passionate about his new talent, and after a couple of jobs he discovered that he was now very good at reading and troubleshooting electrical prints and problems. He would put that talent to use when he was working with electronic controls later in his career back aboard ship.

When two years had passed, Bob called Freddie back to San Francisco and the Burlingame office. Freddie, being a good employee, agreed to take over the Assistant Service Manager's position. The move back to the San Francisco Bay Area was nice in some regards as it meant that Freddie and Cindy could see their family and friends again and enjoy all the restaurants and other amenities of California. Little did they know, though, that this transfer would also bring out some issues which Freddie thought he had overcome.

The move did provide a change of pace, since his new Research and Development and Quality Assurance Testing work exposed Freddie to more of the design aspects of Coen Company. For example, when a design failed to work after being installed in the field, Freddie's job was to handle the necessary modifications or work with the Chief Engineer (the most talented of the design engineers at Coen) to correct the mis-application.

- The Assistant Service Manager work meant that he spent time on the phone helping other Service Engineers with their problems, many of which were related to the electrical drawings which Freddie had become proficient in troubleshooting. Many weekends were spent on the phone helping a fellow Service Engineer. Sometimes Freddie would get up early and go to the Coen Company office on Saturday to catch up on paperwork, only to be trapped on the phone for hours when someone was in trouble. Freddie felt obligated to do what he could for them, having been in the same situation himself when he was working out of Michigan.
- The Research and Development meant that he was working with the Chief Engineer, Coen's most technical engineering person. This involved both designing new products and testing them in the testing yard adjacent to the factory in Burlingame. The idea was that Freddie, who had spent time working in the field with new products, could use his experience to anticipate application problems and offer solutions to reduce the number of issues encountered during start-up of new equipment.
- The Quality Assurance work meant that Freddie and other Service Engineers were tasked with testing equipment before it was shipped from the factory. Their job was to ensure that the models and simulations which the shop technicians made up were truly applicable to the field installation conditions and that

everything was engineered correctly. This brought out some of the political side of things between the engineering (design) and shop (fabrication and assembly) departments, especially when it came to resolving whether any delivery delays were the result of either an engineering problem or a shop delay.

This worked for about two years, but then Freddie realized that some of his bad habits were returning and he was not very happy flying all over the place to fix or start-up Coen equipment in various foreign countries. He was drinking more than usual, and this was causing problems between himself and Cindy. He was exhausted and unhappy, and he was still not making close to the money he could earn by going to sea. That said, he had managed to accomplish quite a bit in learning numerous design and start-up tricks relating to Coen's products, and had mastered the following challenges:

- Honolulu, Hawaii — Boilers for their new gas plant, which burned naphtha to create steam to generate the natural gas sold to their customers on the island. This job required that he and Cindy live in Hawaii for two months to set up the Coen equipment.
- Isfahan, Iran — Installation at an E.I. DuPont polyester plant of an oil-fired duct burner and Coen Fyr-Compak installations on their thermal-oil boilers during the time of the Shah of Iran. This job involved the largest work force in the Middle East, with over 3,000 men working on the jobsite. US contractors were tasked with training former sheep herders to be carpenters, welders, and electricians. The six months they spent there were particularly exciting as Cindy learned Farsi and made friends with locals who invited her and Freddie to their homes to eat and learn their local habits. His posting ended just as the Shah was deposed and 52 Americans were arrested and held captive for a year at the Tehran US embassy.
- Mexico — Copper smelter plant south of Tucson, Arizona using a huge burner to fire over the top of the bath of molten copper ore. The equipment was formerly operated by a US company which had been taken over by the Mexican government years before. The whole operation was crude and poorly maintained. The work was frustrating, and the system was particularly difficult to repair and set properly, since the molten operation of smelting copper could not be shut down.
- Oklahoma & Mexico — Westinghouse PACE250 power plant, designed to fit in a city square block, using Coen duct burners to add sensible heat downstream of a gas turbine and upstream of a waste heat boiler so as to add 50% more efficiency. Installations in Oklahoma and in two locations in Mexico. The Mexico work required Freddie to work six weeks at a time in Veracruz and Torreón during the installation and start-up of the duct burners. This overtime work was not paid in full by Coen, as they did not make any money on the job due to a design fault. This was the beginning of the end for Freddie's Coen career, as he had spent six weeks at a time working 12 to 16 hours per day rebuilding the oil-fired duct burner with modifications to improve reliability. Between jobs in Veracruz and Torreón Freddie spent nearly six months in Mexico. Cindy accompanied him during some of that time to enjoy what was a unique environment in the 1970s. UltimatelBy, the design did not progress due

71

to the rise in cost of diesel fuel, which powered the gas turbines and duct burners in the facility.

One weekend when he was not working, Cindy approached Freddie and told him that she would have to leave if he did not figure out what was troubling him and causing him to abuse alcohol worse than she had ever seen before. Being confronted by Cindy made him realize that he had slid back into his binge drinking routine. To Freddie's surprise, she suggested that he go back to sea and resume working on the ships. He was dumbfounded, as he had thought she wanted him to be home. Quite the opposite: more than anything, she wanted him to be happy with his work and not try to drink his problems away. Upon reflection, Freddie agreed that it was time for him to go back to sea.

Those years had not been wasted, though, as the benefits of the time he'd spent working ashore were plenty! Freddie had added to the character of the Coen Service Engineers thanks to his seagoing experience. He worked as hard as anytime aboard ship, and had used the same creed that his grandmother had taught him about a day's work for a day's pay.

His exposure to the inner workings of Coen had also taught Freddie a great deal about the structure and operation of management in a corporation, and he had even been included in some of the decisions concerning design and improvement of the product line. Most importantly, he had gained invaluable experience regarding anything electrical (and soon to be electronic), plus familiarity with schematics, ladder drawings, and blueprints, which would carry him through the rest of his career. This added confidence to his decision to go back to sea and sail as a Chief Engineer.

Freddie was actually excited and relieved, as he had never been able to get ahead financially despite years of hard work. He and Cindy had built a duo-decagon kit-house using a limited budget, surviving on his meager income and credit card to complete the job. They were using one paycheck for the job and one check for the bills, with minimal money left over for food and gas. As the old saying goes, "ignorance is bliss." Fortunately, Freddie and Cindy had a way of making more money, and the answer was for him to go back to sea. There he could mend their marriage and put their finances back in order!

The other reality was that Freddie had worked in a lower position within Coen Company's management and learned about corporate politics, as well as how policies were established or circumvented. The fact that it was a family-owned company meant that the President could, without any reason, make a binding decision to move someone or essentially stall their growth within the company if he felt it was necessary.

Freddie had also realized that the design of new products was driven by the company's salesmen. They wanted to have something to make new sales, even if the product was not 100% proven in the test yard. This saddled the Service Engineers with the responsibility of actually making such products work in the field. For those men who had worked aboard ship this was nothing new, as all marine engineers have to make do with what they have to keep the ship going. This corporate system, flawed as it was, worked time and time again for Coen due to the expertise of folks like the Service Manager, Bob.

The whole structure of the corporate world was not to Freddie's liking, and he now looked forward to the life of sailing as a Chief Engineer. There was some amount of freedom aboard ship, plus a far better pay rate than working ashore. Freddie was happy that he had learned new skills, but he was not happy about working just as hard and traveling just as much as when he'd gone to sea without making the same money.

So Freddie started networking again and called up his mentor, Lefty, plus a couple of other marine engineers he had met and worked with over the years. What he learned was that he would essentially have to start over with the MEBA, since he had let his dues lapse and was now classified as a Group 2 instead of a Group 1 member. He would be starting out taking any job that was available for at least a year once he was allowed back into the union. Even so, he was looking forward to the life at sea, no matter what the challenges.

COEN COMPANY DUCT BURNER
STICKNEY SEWAGE PLANT

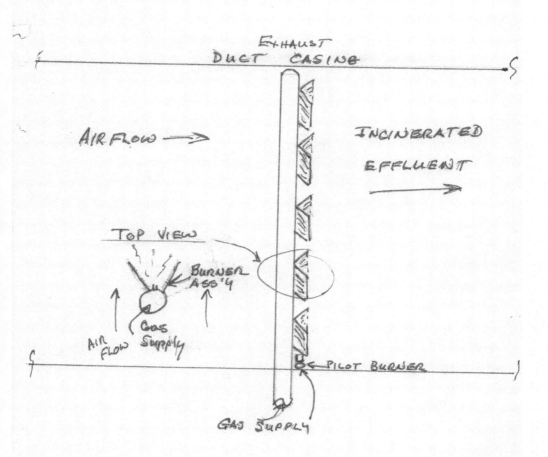

EXHAUST
DUCT CASING

AIRFLOW ⟶

INCINERATED

EFFLUENT

TOP VIEW

BURNER
ASS'Y

AIR
FLOW

Gas
Supply

PILOT BURNER

GAS SUPPLY

COEN COMPANY - OIL-FIRED DUCT BURNER
DETROIT DIESEL ENGINE TESTING PLANT
PACE 250 PROGRAM - US & MEXICO

EXHAUST
DUCT CASING

AIR FLOW →

INCINERATED

EFFLUENT

TOP VIEW →

Burner
Ass'y

Atomizing Air

AIR
FLOOD

Fuel

OIL - AIR ATOMIZED
NOZZLE

GAS FIRED PILOT BURNER

Atomizing
Air

Fuel

WESTINGHOUSE PACE 250 PROGRAM

DESIGNED AND BUILT IN 1970s

DESIGNED TO FIT IN ONE BLOCK

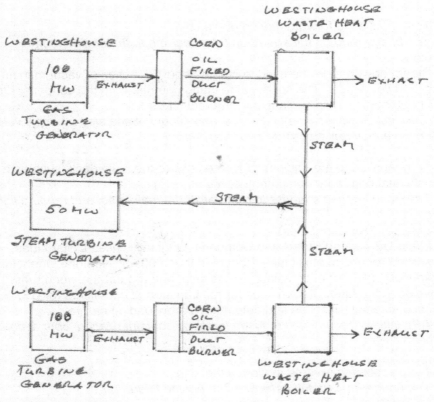

* CORN DUCT BURNER ADDED SENSIBLE HEAT
  TO INCREASE BOILER EFFICIENCY

* SYSTEM WAS TOTALLY COMPUTER CONTROLLED

AB (Able Seaman) –

An endorsement issued by the US Coast Guard to crew members who work for the deck department on US-flagged vessels. They stand watch steering the ship, do maintenance on deck, and tie up and let go the ship.

*The Chief Mate called out all the **AB** seamen to assist with letting go the ship.*

Aft –

Term applied to the back of the ship.

*The crew headed **aft** to tie up the ship.*

Ahead –

Term applied to forward motion of the ship.

*The bridge rang up full **ahead** on the telegraph to the engine room.*

Air Ejector –

Steam-powered device used to create about 30 inches of vacuum in an attached condenser. The condensate being pumped from the condenser to the DC heater acts as the coolant in its internal tubes.

*The First Engineer opened the first and second stage steam supply valves on the main engine **air ejector** to raise vacuum.*

Aloft –

Term applied to the equipment located above the main deck, such as a mast and its attached radar equipment, or the stack(s).

*The Bosun rigged a ladder to climb **aloft** the main mast and repair a light high above the bridge.*

APL (American President Lines) –

Major US-flagged Steamship Company. Originally called Dollar Lines. Absorbed American Mail Lines. Bought in the 1990s by Neptune Orient Lines. Historically a leader in container, cruise ship, and around-the-world runs. Developed the Liner Stack-Trains for rail transport of containers for US transcontinental purposes and automated cargo loading programs.

***APL** initially became the industry leader in containerization, both ashore and afloat.*

Astern –

Term applied to reverse motion of the ship.

*The bridge rang up full **astern** on the engine telegraph.*

Bilge –

The area where water collects at the bottom of the engine room. Located above the double bottom tanks used for (among other things) holding water, oil, and ballast. Includes collection boxes from which water can be pumped over the side.

*The Chief aimed his flashlight towards the **bilge** below the deck plates to check the level of the collected water.*

Bilge Pump –

The pump which removes water from the bilge or other spaces and discharges it over the side into the ocean.

*The Third Engineer started the **bilge pump** to empty the water sitting in the bilge where it had collected in the bilge well by the entrance to the shaft alley.*

Blackgang –

Engine department personnel. Term derives from the days of the coal passers, trimmers, and firemen of the 1870s to 1910s, who were often isolated in dismal living and working conditions. Their blackened faces and bodies, combined with the fact that they worked in "teams" or "gangs," gave rise to the name which is used to this day.

*The Engineers, Oilers, Firemen, and Electricians are all part of the **Blackgang** which operates and maintains the ship's mechanical and electrical equipment.*

Bleed Steam versus Live Steam –

Bleed steam is from a part of a turbine where the steam passing through the turbine is giving up energy but still has heat value to use for secondary purposes like heating water. Live steam is high-pressure steam that is reduced by an automated valve which holds the pressure downstream at a predetermined point. Bleed Steam is more efficient, but it is not available when the ship is not underway.

*The First opened up the low-pressure turbine **bleed steam** that supplied 15 psi steam to heat the feedwater.*

Bloody Thursday (May 9 to July 17, 1934) –

The 86-day San Francisco Waterfront Strike which began the push for unionized waterfront labor in the United States.

*The start of unionization in the US was **Bloody Thursday** in San Francisco, when a strike between the longshoremen and seamen and ship owners resulted in a huge confrontation between the military and the longshoremen and seamen.*

Blowing Tubes –

The act of using high-pressure air or steam to blow unburned fuel (soot) off the tube surfaces while the ship is underway. This practice is done while at sea, and must be coordinated between the deck and engine room so that the wind blows the soot away from the ship. This usually requires the deck to make a course correction.

*When the Second Engineer is **blowing tubes**, the ship command must change course to ensure the soot is blown off to the side instead of dropping onto the deck of the ship.*

Boiler –

Oil-fired steam generator on ships which supplies steam to operate main steam turbines and steam-driven generators. On Victory ships the pressure was 440 psi, delivered superheated (for turbine use) and desuperheated (for pumps and auxiliary equipment use).

*The **boiler** on a steam ship is the heart of the engineering plant that provides the energy to run the ship.*

Break Bulk Ship (aka Stick Ship or General Cargo Ship) –

Another term used for cargo ship designs predating the era of containerization. (See definition of "general cargo ship" below.)

*Victory ships and other **break bulk** vessels were designed to load and unload individual pieces of cargo.*

Bulkhead –

Term applied to the wall of a space or room.

*The engineer hung his boiler suit on the hook embedded in the **bulkhead** after drying it in the fidley.*

Bull Wiper –

The lead wiper who is most experienced or picked by the First Engineer to lead the three Wipers.

*The First Engineer told the **Bull Wiper** to organize a cleaning gang with the other wipers to clean up after the repairs to the piping.*

Bunker Oil (aka C Fuel Oil) –

The closest thing to road tar used aboard ship as fuel to burn in an engine or boiler. The dregs of the refinery business, it has to be heated to at least 200 degrees Fahrenheit prior to use to allow for proper atomization.

*The **bunker oil** received from the fuel barge was heated to about 180 degrees Fahrenheit so that it would flow from the barge to the ship's fuel tanks.*

Captain (aka Master) –

By maritime law and by company rules, the person ultimately responsible for the operation of the ship. All department heads report to the Captain, and he is responsible for the safe operation of the vessel and navigation by the crew.

*The **Captain** is in command of the ship whenever he is on the bridge.*

Chain of Command –

The military-type hierarchy aboard ship, with the Captain at the top and the lowest posting, such as Wiper, at the bottom. It dictates who is in charge of whom, and of whom permission must be asked.

*The **chain of command** puts the Captain at the head of the crew, and all others are under his direct command.*

Charley Noble –

The stack from the oil-fired galley stove. The Victory ships still had oil-fired stoves when they were first activated, but these were later converted to electrical stoves. If the stack was not maintained, it could back up and cover the galley with soot.

*Grey smoke drifted out of the **Charley Noble** stack from the galley's oil-fired stove.*

Chief –

Term applied to the head of the Deck Department (Chief Mate), Engine Department (Chief Engineer), or Stewards Department (Chief Steward).

*The term **"Chief"** can apply to any one of three persons on a ship, such as the Chief Engineer, Chief Mate, or Chief Steward.*

Coal Passer –

On coal-burning ships during the period from 1870 to 1913, a man who brought coal from the storage bunkers to the furnaces, and also removed the ashes after it was burned.

The Coal Passer was a member of the Blackgang, part of the engine department crew responsible for feeding coal to the boilers during the days of coal-fired ships.

Compressor, Air –

A type of pump used to produce high-pressure air for on-deck work or air soot blowers.

The air compressor on a Victory ship supplies air to blow soot in the boilers.

Compressor, Refrigeration –

A type of coolant pump used in stores boxes, drinking fountains, and refrigerators. Refrigeration compressors originally used R12 Freon as the refrigerant.

The refrigeration compressor pumps refrigerant to cool the food stored in the ship's food storage boxes.

Condenser *(Machinery)* – Main Engine (Main) or Turbo-Generator (Auxiliary)

Water-in-tube heat exchanger used to convert the spent steam from a steam turbine back into condensate (liquid). A partial vacuum is created by the difference in temperature between the cold seawater inside the tubes and the hot steam condensing on the exterior of the tubes. This vacuum is increased and maintained by the two-stage air ejector which serves to remove any non-condensable vapors from the system.

The main condenser is cooled by seawater fed from the main circulator. This seawater flows through tubes, with the steam from the turbine(s) flowing and condensing around the outside of the tubes.

Condenser *(Refrigeration)* –

The heat exchanger in the refrigeration system that uses seawater in-tube as a cooling medium to convert the vaporized refrigerant back into a liquid as it passes around the outside of the tubes. This is the place in the refrigeration system where the heat from the refrigeration boxes is given up to the seawater cooling.

The amount of seawater flowing through the refrigeration condenser helps keep the refrigeration compressor head pressure in range and keeps that system in balance.

Container *(Box Ship)* –

Term applied to a trailer specifically designed to be lifted aboard a ship and set into a hatch, on top of a hatch cover, or on top of another container. The perfection of containerization is attributed to Malcolm McClean, who containerized the Vietnam War and changed the entire marine industry. Container ships were developed and put into general use starting in the late 1960s, and containers are now the primary type of cargo being transported by ships worldwide.

Container ships became the principal design of ship in the late 1960s due to the lower cost of handling cargo compared to break bulk or general cargo type ships.

Cosmoline –

Rust preventative applied to ships before they are laid up in the Reserve Fleet. This process plus others, such as dehumidification, have kept ships in layup free of rust and deterioration for decades.

Cosmoline is used to protect metal parts of a ship during the time it is laid up in the Maritime Administration Reserve Fleet in Suisun Bay near San Francisco.

DC Heater (Direct Contact/Deareating Feed Heater) –

The water reservoir fitted to the top of the engine room which supplies the boiler feed pumps with water. This device also heats and releases the trapped oxygen from the condensate pumped from the condenser by the condensate pump.

*The **DC heater** performs multiple functions upon the feedwater supplied to the boilers. It both heats it and reaerates it, while also serving as a reservoir for the boiler feed pumps.*

Deck –

Term applied to the floor of a space or room.

*Walking on a steel **deck** will create problems with your knees over time.*

Deck Plates –

The diamond plate steel flooring which the crew walks on. Covers the piping and bilges below. "Hitting the deck plates" means going to work in the engine room.

*The **deck plates** are diamond steel plate screwed to angle bar frames about three feet above the bilges in the engine room.*

Double Bottom –

The tanks located just within the skin of the ship's hull. The tops of these tanks underlie the bilge area in the engine room and the bottom of the holds.

*The **double bottom** tanks are those located between the steel hull of the ship, which is exposed to the ocean, and the bilges in the engine room and cargo holds.*

Duct Burner –

An in-line gas- or oil-fired burner assembly fitted to the inside of an exhaust duct. A typical arrangement involved a group of vertical pipes spaced about 18 inches apart and fitted from the bottom to the top of the duct. Such burners were used to incinerate effluent or add sensible heat to a downstream device.

*Coen Company built many customer-designed **duct burners** in the 1970s.*

Dunnage –

The debris left over after loading or unloading the ship in port. In the days of general cargo (break bulk or stick) ships with cargo booms and cranes, this often consisted of lumber and nails which had been used to set and hold cargo in place within a ship's holds. The longshoremen removed this and laid it on the deck, and the crew had to dispose of it over the side after the ship took departure in the ocean. It might also include wood, cardboard, fasteners, and dirt left over from the loading or unloading process.

*The debris left on the deck after cargo operations on a break bulk ship is **dunnage**, and it was thrown over the side once the ship was at sea.*

Ebb Tide –

When the tide moves out to sea and the water level drops.

*As the **ebb tide** moved the ship down relative to the shore, the gangway changed from a vertical climb to an almost horizontal one.*

Endorsements –

The permits issued by the US Coast Guard allowing Unlicensed personnel to work as Wipers, Oilers, Firemen, etc.

*The Unlicensed Blackgang members were given approval to sail in their classification, such as Wiper, Oiler, or Fireman, according to their US Coast Guard **endorsements**.*

Fidley –

The uppermost part of the engine room which is open to the skylights or exhaust fans. This ventilation space allows hot air to escape from the engine room.

*The Chief Engineer could enter the **fidley** from his quarters, allowing for fast access to the engine room in times of emergency.*

Fireman-Watertender –

On old ships that lacked automated systems this job actually belonged to two people. One, the Watertender, would be responsible for maintaining the water level in the boiler. Another, the Fireman, would be responsible for handling the fire room and the oil burners and such. After the introduction of automated water level controls, these jobs were combined. Such was the operation aboard Victory ships.

*The **Fireman-Watertender** is responsible for the operation of the boilers as endorsed by the US Coast Guard.*

First Engineer (aka 1st Assistant Engineer) –

The engineer who runs the Blackgang and is directly responsible to the Chief Engineer. Many are also capable of sailing as a Chief Engineer and hold a Chief Engineer's license.

*The **First Engineer** is responsible for running the Blackgang and reports directly to the Chief Engineer.*

Flood Tide –

When the tide comes inland and the water level rises.

*The ship rises with the water during the **flood tide**, and the gangway climb becomes more vertical.*

Focsle (aka Fo'c'sle or Foc'sle) –

Term applied to the rooms aboard ships. Also used to describe the rooms used by Unlicensed crew members.

*The **focsle** of a seaman is a room about 10 feet by 15 feet, with a toilet, shower, sink, and some drawers for clothes.*

Forward –
　　Term applied to either the front of the ship or moving ahead.
　　*The **forward** part of the ship is where the anchor is stowed and dropped when in port.*
GAA (General Agency Agreement) –
　　A General Agency Agreement contract between the Maritime Administration and a steamship company which, as a general agent, exercises administrative control over a government owned ship.
　　*During the Vietnam War, Victory ships were run by many West Coast steamship companies under a **GAA** contract.*
Galley –
　　The kitchen on the ship where all the food is prepared and work is done by the Stewards Department.
　　*The **galley** is the kitchen section of the ship that feeds the crew.*
General Cargo Ship (aka Break Bulk Ship or Stick Ship) –
　　Predominant ship design in the United States from the 1960s to the 1980s. Such ships featured hatches fitted with cargo-handling gear, such as long wire-rope booms, which allowed individual pieces of cargo to be lifted to or from the dock to the hatch levels. Once aboard, this cargo was then moved manually or with forklifts to areas to the forward, port, starboard, and aft sides of the hatch openings. This design was improved upon by container vessels, which made cargo less expensive to load and unload from the ships. After the 1980s, all serious shipping companies converted to container ships and general cargo ships were scrapped or used for special purposes only.
　　***General cargo** ships, also called break bulk or stick ships, were the primary type of cargo-handling vessels in the late 1960s.*
Hatch (aka Hold) –
　　The opening in a ship through which cargo was stowed or removed.
　　On general cargo ships (such as older Victory, Liberty, C2, and C3 vessels) the arrangement was open all the way to the tank tops (on top of the ship's keel) and separated at various levels to allow stowage of cargo. Each level could be fitted with removable beams and hatch boards or pontoons, which made a solid floor covering the opening to the level below.
　　On more modern vessels, shipping containers are stacked directly atop one another within the hold. Each hatch is topped by a solid cover on which up to six additional shipping containers may also be stacked
　　*The **hatch** is the area of the ship where the cargo hold is located. On older ships the **hatch** was covered with wood and canvas, and on new ships it has a large steel cover.*
Hawsepipe *(Anchor Chain)* –
　　The steel tube on the bow that the anchor chain is led through to connect to the anchor on the exterior of the hull.
　　*The **hawsepipe** is the tube on the bow that the anchor chain travels through to raise and lower the anchor.*

Hawsepipe *(Non-Academy Licensed Officers)* –
   The term applied to persons who do not go to a Maritime Academy to get their license from the US Coast Guard. Instead they advance from the lowest unlicensed job, getting higher endorsements from the US Coast Guard until they eventually gain enough time and experience to sit for their US Coast Guard license.
   *The **hawsepipe** engineers are those who started out as Wipers and worked their way up to a license, instead of graduating from a merchant marine academy.*

Hold (aka Hatch) –
   Another term that applies to the hatches on a ship where cargo is stowed. (See definition of "hatch" above.)
   *Cargo **holds** were arranged to accept individual pieces of cargo during break bulk cargo ship days. Later, in the 1960s, cargo **holds** were designed with cells which guide containers to stack on top of each other.*

HP Turbine –
   High-pressure turbine on a steam-powered ship which receives the superheated steam from the boilers. This drives the high-speed part of the reduction gear which reduces the speed to the line shaft that turns the propeller.
   *The **HP turbine** receives steam directly from the boilers via the throttle operated by the ship's engineers.*

Ladder (aka Catwalk) –
   This term applies to steps both on deck and inside the ship, as well as in the engine room. These steps are fitted with handrails on both sides to ensure that seamen do not fall while the ship is moving.
   *The **ladders** in the engine room wind around the huge pieces of equipment such as the DC heater and the boilers.*

Line Shaft –
   The flanged shafting connecting the reduction gear to the propeller is located in the shaft alley on line shaft bearings spaced down the length of the shaft alley. The shaft penetrates the aft end of the ship and is supported by the stern tube, which has packing on the inside to prevent flooding of the shaft alley.
   *The Chief Engineer walked the shaft alley, checking the **line shaft** that connects the reduction gear to the propeller.*

Longshoreman –
   A member of the unions that have for decades handled the loading and unloading of ships.
   *The **longshoremen** are the men who have historically loaded and unloaded cargo aboard ships, and are organized by a union.*

LP Turbine –
   On a steam-powered ship, the low-pressure turbine which receives steam from the HP turbine and discharges it to the condenser to be converted to condensate. On the forward end of the LP turbine rotor is the astern turbine,

which drives the ship in reverse (aka astern). This turbine drives the low-speed part of the reduction gear which turns the line shaft that turns the propeller.

*The **LP turbine** is huge in comparison to the HP turbine, and it houses the astern element which moves the ship opposite the normal (ahead) direction.*

Main Circulator Pump –

The primary device used to pump seawater from the ocean through the main condenser in order to cool the spent steam and turn it back into liquid condensate.

*The **main circulator pump** forces water through the main condenser tubes to cool the spent steam as it exits the turbine cavity.*

Matson Steamship Company –

One of the few remaining US-owned, US-flagged steamship companies. Has supplied the Hawaiian Islands with goods and cargo for many decades, and also furnishes inter-island cargo transportation.

***Matson Steamship Company** has dominated the business of supplying cargo from the West Coast US to the Hawaiian Islands since the time of the early settlers.*

Messman –

The waiter on a ship who took orders from the crew and brought them their food. This person was part of the crew for the Deck Department, the Engine Department, and the Officer's mess rooms. Once the typical crew shrank from 40-plus to under 20 individuals, this practice was stopped and meals began to be served cafeteria-style, with a reduced staff in charge of food preparation.

*The **messmen** enabled formal dining aboard ships, as they would set tables with tablecloths, silverware, plates, glasses, and cups.*

MFOW (Marine Firemen, Oilers, and Watertenders Union) –

West Coast union for engine department (Blackgang) unlicensed crew.

*Lefty's contacts in the **MFOW** allowed him to put together an exceptional Blackgang crew.*

MSC (Military Sealift Command) –

The civilian-crewed organization which is in charge of the replenishment and military transport ships for all US military services. Originally known as the Army Transport Service, then the Military Sea Transport Service. The combined forces of MSTS and others were established during the Vietnam War and still exist today, with global presence and many different kinds of ships manned by civilian crew.

***MSC** controls the ships that support the US Navy and other branches of the military, plus the civilian crew, maintenance, and operation of the ships.*

MSTS (Military Sea Transport Service) –

Former name of Military Sealift Command, from 1949 to the Vietnam War era.

*For months following the French defeat at Dien Bien Phu, **MSTS** provided sea passage for the Vietnamese escaping from North Vietnam to South Vietnam.*

Nameboard –

A plaque placed on the side of the bridge which identifies the name of the ship. Usually made of wood.

*The ship's **nameboard** is located on the bridge wing.*

NMU (National Maritime Union) –

The National Maritime Union was established in 1937 and was known as one of the best unions of Unlicensed tankermen in the United States. Due to the collapse of the shipping industry after the Vietnam War, the union fell upon hard times and eventually merged with the SIU in 2001.

*The **NMU** supplied Unlicensed tankermen to man the Keystone tanker ships.*

Oiler –

This position originally belonged to men who were responsible for oiling the gear on a reciprocating engine, but as ships became fitted with turbines the Oiler became a watchstander who made rounds and took readings hourly. Many were very talented and would not allow the Engineer to make out the log or do equipment changes.

*A seaman with a US Coast Guard endorsement that allows the Blackgang member to sail in the engine department, the **Oiler** works directly for the Engineer on the watch.*

OS (Ordinary Seaman) –

An endorsement issued by the US Coast Guard to a seaman who works on deck and performs all the menial jobs such as focsle cleanup, chipping and painting, and working on projects with the Bosun. This is the lowest rating for the deck department.

*The **Ordinary Seaman** is the deck hand who does all the cleanup work on deck.*

Overhead –

Term applied to the ceiling or inside room top covering.

*The **overhead** of the room had only a single light; the other lamps were positioned on a desk and on the bunk.*

Pacific Far East Lines –

A major West Coast company which ran a very lucrative trade route to Asia, but made a poor decision to build LASH (Lighter Aboard Ship Handling) ships instead of container vessels. This mistake eventually caused them to go under in the 1970s.

***Pacific Far East Lines** operated break bulk ships reliably and profitably for many years, but did not adapt to containerization and eventually went bankrupt.*

Pilot –

The trained and licensed Captain who navigates the ship between a berthing place and the ocean. Most have been a Master aboard ship for a number of years. All are required to undergo an apprenticeship with a seasoned Pilot of many years before being allowed to Pilot on their own. The only person who can remove this person from command during the maneuvering of the ship to or from the sea is the ship's Captain.

*The **Pilot** takes control of the ship from the dock to the pilot station outside the Golden Gate Bridge.*

Port –

Term applied to the side of the ship on the left when facing forward.

*The lifeboat for the Chief Engineer was on the **port** side of the ship.*

Purifier –

High speed centrifugal device which separates water and debris from oil. In the marine industry, it is used to remove water from lubricating oil for the main engine, and from fuel oil on motor ships.

*The **purifier** is necessary to remove any water and collected debris from the engine oil.*

Purser –

The ship's clerk who works directly for the Captain. A multi-tasked crew member who handles the money, draws up the Articles which the crew members sign, and pays off the crew at the end of a voyage. He might also handle first aid when necessary.

*The **Purser** signed on the new Chief Engineer according to the message sent by the office.*

PX –

A commissary on a United States Army post. A retail store which sells equipment and provisions, usually to military personnel or their dependents.

*The ship had **PX** goods for the military stationed in Vietnam.*

Radio Operator –

During the days of the Vietnam sealift, the person who stood a watch to listen for any emergencies from other ships and sent all the ship's information to the office for the Captain. Almost all communication was carried out in Morse code, as there were no satellite phones, GPS, or other advanced communication technologies until the 1980s.

*The **Radio Operator** had to listen to Morse code daily for hours in case there was a ship in distress which needed assistance.*

Reciprocating –

Machinery that moves up and down, such as the steam-driven pumps on a Victory ship. Alternative to motor-driven centrifugal pumps, which rotate.

*The **reciprocating** engine was installed on the Liberty ships during WWII, when they were delivering one ship per day.*

Reefer –

Refrigeration equipment which allows ships' stores to be kept for long periods of time. Term also applied to an Unlicensed crew member whose job was to maintain refrigerated containers, which became the norm in the 1970s.

***Reefers** are kept cool by refrigerant circulated through the system by a pump. They allow ships to keep stores for months, and have been used ever since the Vietnam war period.*

Sailing Board –

The official notification posted at the gangway 24 hours prior to departure. Informs the crew of the ship's next destination, as well as the date and time (in military 24-hour notation) it will be leaving the current port.

*The Captain set the **sailing board** for the ship to sail at 0600 hours the next morning.*

Sensible Heat –

Heat which can be sensed or felt as it moves into and raises the temperature of a system or substance. Alternative to latent heat, which moves into a substance and changes its phase (for example, melting solid ice into liquid water) instead of raising its temperature.

*Coen duct burners could be used to add **sensible heat** to a system.*

Shipping Card –

When an engineer leaves a ship after completing a job, they register with their Union and receive a shipping card. This card lists the date on which it was issued, and is used to apply for the engineer's next job. When multiple engineers apply for a position, seniority is determined by the dates on their shipping cards, with the job going to the engineer with the oldest shipping card. As a result, engineers who are willing to stay on the beach for months gain the ability to pick whatever job they desire.

*Freddie put his **shipping card** on the counter of the dispatcher to bid on the Second Engineer's job on the* Azalea City.

Singling Up –

The act of removing all of a ship's lines from the pier, except for one on the bow and one on the stern, in preparation for a ship's departure from a port. The ship might be assisted by a tugboat to keep it alongside the pier and prevent it from breaking loose.

*The Captain alerted the Mates on the bow and the stern to **single up**, as the tug assist was alongside to help the ship get underway.*

Sponson –

An addition to the side of a ship which allows the tracks for a gantry crane's wheels to roll the assembly forward and aft for positioning over a row of containers.

*The gantry crane tracks were welded to **sponsons** on the sides of the ship.*

Stack –

The structure through which the exhaust from boilers or diesels and relief valves vents to the atmosphere. The company insignia is painted or attached to both sides of this chimney.

*Smoke poured out of the **stack** as the Second Engineer blew tubes on the boiler.*

Starboard –

Term applied to the side of the ship on the right when facing forward.

*The lifeboat for the Captain is on the **starboard** side of the ship.*

States Line Steamship Company –

Organization which ran a white fleet from 1919 to the 1980s. Their ships were well run and had great trade routes, but the decision to build Ro-Ro (Roll On-Roll Off) type ships instead of container vessels led to their downfall and eventual demise in the 1980s.

*The **States Line Steamship Company** had a great white fleet for decades, but they failed to adapt to the containerized cargo design and went bankrupt.*

Steamship Company –

The term applies to any company which owns and operates ships. In the 1960s, roughly 50 US-owned companies (including APL, States Line, and Pacific Far East Lines) had fleets of ships, but today only a handful of steamship companies are US-owned and -flagged. Except for Matson Navigation, all of the major companies that operated out of the San Francisco waterfront in the 1960s are now gone.

*The **steamship company** business in the USA was lucrative until the 1960s, when the need to economize on crew costs and adapt to container-type operation decided who would stay in business.*

Steering Gear –

The equipment used to move the rudder. Fitted above the rudder itself, this gear is usually operated remotely from the bridge. The steering gear also has emergency modes enabling the steering engine room to be operated locally if the bridge steering equipment malfunctions.

*The **steering gear** is operated from the bridge and executed in the steering engine room in the aft part of the ship, where the rudder is located.*

Switchboard –

The electrical control board which allows the output of the electrical generator to be connected to all the ship's electrical equipment via circuit breakers. On Victory ships the power was direct current (DC), but on newer vessels the power is alternating current (AC), since controls on AC allow multiple generators to be synchronized and run in parallel.

*The **switchboard** in the engine room controls the electrical power flowing to all the users on the ship.*

Telegraph –

A communication device which allows the bridge to issue commands to any location capable of steering the rudder or operating the engine. The rudder is ordinarily steered from the bridge but may be operated from the steering engine room during emergencies. Repeaters were located in the throttle platform and in the fireroom on old steam ships, while the repeaters in new motor vessels are located in the engine control room and at engine side.

*The bridge uses the **telegraph** to notify the engine room of the direction and speed they want to move the ship while maneuvering into and out of port.*

Trimmer –

A man who would wheelbarrow coal from the bunker storage area to the furnace crew for putting into the boiler furnace.

*The **Trimmer*** *was a member of the Blackgang in the days of coal-fired boilers, who helped with the coal fed into the furnace of the boiler.*

Turbo-Generator –

A turbine-driven generator such as is used on steam-powered ships. The size and power of the generators allowed for 100% electrical-driven motors, pumps, and other equipment aboard general cargo ships in their day. The turbine ran at a high speed and was reduced by a reduction gear coupled to the generator that operated at 440 VAC, 3 phase, 60 cycle delivery to the switchboard.

*The **turbo-generator*** *ran on 440-psi steam and delivered 440-volt AC power to the ship's switchboard to power all the ship's electrical gear.*

United States Lines –

Dating back to the 1930s, this premier cruise line company ran a very successful business between the East Coast of the US and Europe until airplanes became the primary mode of transportation for that route. Their cargo trade routes were international in scope, but they defied conventional wisdom by starting those round-the-world routes heading east across the Atlantic, rather than west across the Pacific. Along with the huge, underpowered, and trouble-prone container vessels they designed and built, this mistake led to their downfall, and they went out of business in 1986.

*The **United States Lines*** *operated the fastest and most luxurious ships in the heyday of the trans-Atlantic ocean liner operation. They later shifted into container operation, but neglected to adapt to the proven technology and eventually went bankrupt.*

USCG (United States Coast Guard) –

The US government agency which inspects and provides oversight in the operation and design of US-flagged vessels. This agency is also responsible for testing and awarding Licenses to Mates and Engineers, plus providing endorsements to Unlicensed seamen.

*The **US Coast Guard*** *is responsible for all things related to US Merchant Mariners, including licensing, endorsements, and inspections.*

Winch –

The deck machinery which allows the crew to pull lines aboard the ship when letting go or tying up the ship. Older designs used steam power, and all modern-day ships use electrical motors.

*The drum on the **winch*** *is used to pull in the lines for tying up the ship when it is docking in a port.*

Windlass –

The deck machine which is mounted on the bow to haul in and let go the anchor and anchor chain. It is also used as a winch for bringing in lines. Those on some older ships used steam power, but on modern ships an electric motor is used.

*The **windlass*** *has the ability to raise or lower the anchor. It can be operated by either steam or an electric motor.*

Wiper –

The lowest position in the Unlicensed engineering department union. This person does all the dirty work of cleaning, painting, and providing necessary labor for all the jobs in the engine room.

The **Wiper** is the lowest classification of endorsement by the US Coast Guard for the Blackgang. They do all the dirty work in the engine room.

AUTHOR'S PAGE

The storyline and characters in this introduction to the Blackgang are inspired by my years of going to sea as a marine engineer. I graduated from the California Maritime Academy in 1965 and was lucky to have been introduced to the industry at that time when there was a high demand for engineers aboard ships servicing the Vietnam War sealift. In the 23 years that I went to sea, I was able to sail aboard vintage vessels, such as Victory ships, and later aboard modern-day motor container vessels.

My sincere desire is that this book will provide some insight into the workings and lifestyle of the members of the Blackgang, who are essentially invisible to the general public. Without these men and women the ships would not operate, be maintained, get repaired, or move from one port to another. They deserve recognition and appreciation for their daily efforts to keep the ships and goods we depend upon moving around the world.

Future books will continue to expand upon the Life and Times of Freddie and his experiences aboard ship. Life at sea evolved greatly during the 1980s, when the US Merchant Marine made some big changes coinciding with the end of the Vietnam War, the move to containerize the US-flagged fleet, and a shift from steam- to motor-powered vessels.

If you have questions or comments, please feel free to send me an email and I will reply in a timely manner. I hope that you have enjoyed these books, and that you will join me again for future stories of Freddie's life as a marine engineer.

James Sundfors
Retired Chief Engineer
Email: james.sundfors@gmail.com

Made in the USA
Middletown, DE
17 July 2021